INSTRUMENTS
and
PROCESS CONTROL

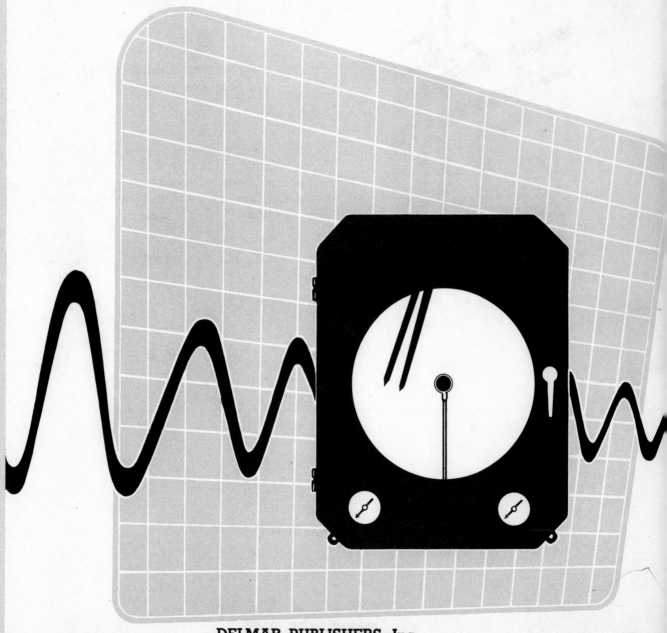

DELMAR PUBLISHERS, Inc.
ALBANY, NEW YORK

INSTRUMENTS AND PROCESS CONTROL

1947

A PUBLICATION OF

**THE NEW YORK STATE VOCATIONAL AND
PRACTICAL ARTS ASSOCIATION**

SECOND PRINTING

PRINTED IN THE UNITED STATES OF AMERICA

DELMAR PUBLISHERS, Inc.
ALBANY, NEW YORK

Preface

This monograph, INSTRUMENTS and PROCESS CONTROL, was prepared in the Curriculum Laboratory at Cornell University, Ithaca, New York, in cooperation with the Taylor Instrument Companies of Rochester, New York.

The monograph was developed by Ralph E. Clarridge, J. S. Detwiler, George E. Heller, and Richard N. Pond, of the Taylor Instrument Companies, and B. Chester Delahooke of the Curriculum Laboratory.

The work of preparing the material for publication was done by the various members of the Curriculum Laboratory staff. Drawings were prepared by Russell M. Terry. Typing and proofreading of the manuscript were done by Olga S. Schuster. The project was under the immediate direction of Lynn A. Emerson, Director of the Curriculum Laboratory.

Acknowledgment is made for the cooperation of the Taylor Instrument Companies, and for the interest and help of Mr. R. E. Olson of that organization. Appreciation is also expressed to Mr. E. D. Haigler of the Foxboro Company, Foxboro, Massachusetts, for many valuable suggestions, and to the College of Engineering, Cornell University, for providing the facilities which made this project possible.

Acknowledgment is due to the following instrument manufacturers who furnished illustrations and other data:

The Bristol Company	Waterbury, Conn.
Brown Instrument Company	Philadelphia, Pa.
The Foxboro Company	Foxboro, Mass.
Fisher Governor Company	Marshalltown, Iowa
Fulton Sylphon Company	Knoxville, Tenn.
Mason-Neilan Regulator Company	Boston, Mass.
Moore Products Company	Philadelphia, Pa.
C. J. Tagliabue Company	Brooklyn, N. Y.
Taylor Instrument Companies	Rochester, N. Y.

Albany, N. Y.

September, 1945

EUGENE D. FINK, *Chairman*

Publications Committee New York State
Vocational and Practical Arts Association

Instrument Technology Series

FUNDAMENTALS OF PRESSURE AND TEMPERATURE INSTRUMENTS

Principles of manufacture, operation and maintenance of instruments used for process control are described in simple terminology in FUNDAMENTALS OF PRESSURE AND TEMPERATURE INSTRUMENTS.

This book includes *Information Sheets* (Part I) and *Laboratory Units* (Part II) which first deal with physical and chemical laws affecting pressure and temperature measuring and recording instruments; and later, with the operation and application of instruments and accessories for controlling manufacturing processes.

232 pages (7¾ x 10); contains line drawings, photographs, phantom outlines of instruments; and a complete series of thirty-one laboratory units

INSTRUMENTS AND PROCESS CONTROL

Basic control theory, and methods and mechanisms for obtaining various control effects, are described in INSTRUMENTS AND PROCESS CONTROL so that the function of each device is readily understood. Practical industrial installations of control systems, controller adjustments, and checking and testing procedures are given for different process industries.

233 pages (8½ x 11); includes 198 schematic drawings, line drawings and photographs; and two Appendices (I—Glossary; II—Advanced Control Theory)

REFER TO BACK COVER FOR ADDITIONAL TITLES

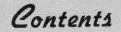

Contents

INFORMATION SHEETS

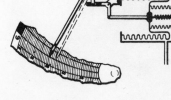

Information Sheets

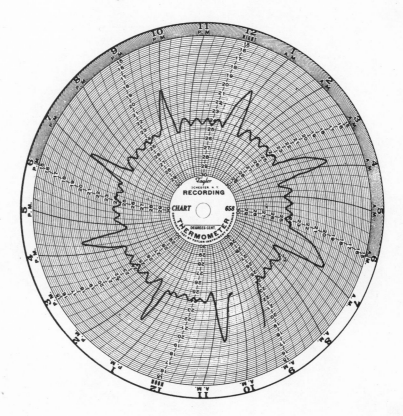

Information Sheet 1   INDUSTRIAL PROCESSES

Very few raw materials are usable in their natural state. Petroleum and various other minerals must be purified and refined before they are of commercial use. Agricultural products, such as wheat and corn, must be cleaned and treated before they are satisfactory for many purposes. The operations which are performed on the various materials to make them more widely useful are called industrial processes .

Courtesy of Foxboro Co.

There are an infinite variety of industrial processes. The water supply of large cities is "processed" before it is used. So is the sewage before it is released. Wood pulp is processed into paper. When air is heated and humidified, it passes through a process. Generally speaking, industrial processes are limited to those operations which take place on a relatively large scale. It is these processes which are the subject of this monograph.

Some industrial processes are simple, so that the men and machinery performing the operation require little supervision or control. The vast majority of processes require a control of the time, temperature, pressure or other physical factors influencing the quality of the final product, in addition to the control of the quantities of constituent raw materials. To be specific, in making bread, the quality and quantity of each raw material for a given batch must be carefully measured. The ingredients must be mixed (a unit process) in the proper sequence. The bread must rise for a time at a suitable temperature (a unit process), and finally it must be baked (a unit process) under the correct conditions. The subsequent cooling, wrapping and delivery of the bread are not generally looked upon as unit processes for they do not affect the basic character of the, bread. As will be seen from this example, the process of making bread can be divided into several "unit processes" or single operations in a sequence required to produce a finished article.

For the purpose of studying processes and applying suitable control systems to them, it is often helpful to break them down into "units". For example, the baking of bricks is not unlike the baking of bread, since both temperature and time are involved in both cases. The fact that both the temperature and time are considerably different does not prevent the application of the knowledge gained on the one to the other. Yet it will be noted that while the baking processes are similar, there is no unit process in the manufacture of bricks corresponding to the rising of the bread.

Industrial processes are controlled to obtain the best possible finished product with the lowest possible processing cost. Accurate

Information Sheet 1

control insures a uniform quality which is equally important.

Referring again to our homely example, if quantities are not accurately controlled in the bread mix, the quality may be below standard or an unnecessary amount of the expensive ingredients may be used. If the bread is not allowed to rise for the proper time at a suitable temperature, the loaf will be heavy or entirely too light. Finally, the product may be poor or even unsaleable if the baking is not correctly controlled. Thus, in this particular process, time and temperature are as important as the quality and quantity of the ingredients.

Process control may be either manual or automatic. Since on repeated process cycles human control is not too dependable, there has been a definite trend toward automatic control. Every housewife will testify to the difficulty in keeping an oven temperature "just right" without a thermostat. It is easy to "forget" a process which is several hours long, or to allow it to deviate too far from the desired point. While automatic control systems are not perfect, they are far more dependable generally than manual control and they have come into use wherever they can be economically justified.

Of course, it is easier to justify the expenditure for automatic control systems on large processes where great quantities of materials are handled, since a single failure in manual control might easily result in a waste of raw materials which would more than pay for a good automatic system. Inadequate manual control may result in a non-uniformity of product so that customers are lost and profits reduced. It is safe to say that automatic control will continue to replace manual control on industrial processes

The variables which are most frequently controlled on industrial processes are those which are most easily measured. The quantity and composition of the raw materials and the time of each unit process are basic. The quality control is usually a laboratory matter, while the time control is simple whether it be manual or automatic. Quantity control may be by weight, using scales, balances, etc., or by volume, using tanks, level and flow instruments. Many unit processes also involve temperature pressure and other similar variables which are as important as time in many chemical reactions, separations and distillations.

Uniformity, quality, cost, waste and the like are not directly controllable for they cannot be easily measured during the process. These are indirectly controlled variables since they are responsive to some of the other directly controlled variables outlined above. Generally speaking, the directly controlled variables are important only in so far as they affect the quality and cost of the final product.

Information Sheet 1

Controller mechanisms, like most other modern machines, have passed through various stages of development. The first controllers were largely mechanically operated, but as process requirements became more exacting, better results were possible when certain combinations of mechanical, electrical, pneumatic and hydraulic devices were used. Manufacturers now choose from many combinations of mechanical, hydraulic, pneumatic and electrical devices to provide the control needed for a specific installation. Usually, the characteristics of the installation itself determine which type of device is needed. For example, where extreme fire hazard is encountered, a pneumatic type might be preferred to an electrical type, or where extreme pressures are required, hydraulic operation might be indicated. High temperatures might indicate electrical control.

Recently there has been a considerable increase in the number of controllers using the electronics principle of operation. Probably this field has not yet reached its stage of greatest development.

Information Sheet 2   THE IMPORTANCE OF MEASUREMENT TO CONTROL

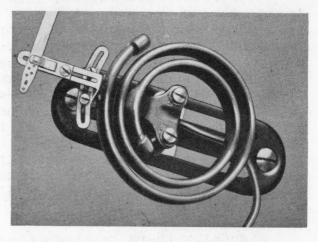

Courtesy of Taylor Instrument Cos.

The fundamental purpose of an automatic controller is to maintain at a predetermined setting point the condition it regulates. This is accomplished by utilizing a measuring system to detect variations in the controlled medium and having this measuring system actuate a mechanical device for applying a corrective action to overcome the disturbance which caused the initial variation. Regardless of the complications of an automatic controller, there must always be a measuring system which, either directly, or through suitable relays, actuates a source of power for accomplishing the desired control.

It follows, therefore, that in order to produce accurate control of a variable, it must first be accurately measured. The measuring element or system cannot be subjected to excessive friction or dead-spot, otherwise the control obtainable will suffer. The quality of a controller is judged to a large extent by the accuracy of its measuring system in reproducing the true condition of the measured and controlled medium. Thus, if due to friction, or dead-spot, the measuring system does not respond to a change in the medium being controlled, the controller cannot be expected to develop a corrective action. The result of this is that a still greater change must take place before the measuring element even starts to actuate the control mechanism to bring about a correction or compensation for the deviation. The type of control obtainable under these conditions is never stable, and on many applications would be very undesirable. An example of the foregoing might be as shown in Fig. 1.

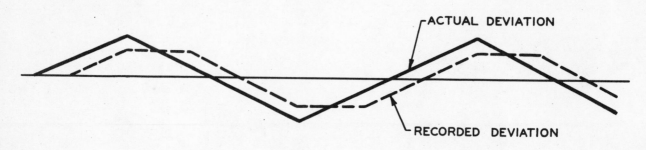

ACTUAL DEVIATION

RECORDED DEVIATION

Fig. 1

Information Sheet 2

If, for example, a temperature measuring system has a friction and dead-spot error due to the linkage construction equal to 2% of the range of the instrument, the actual temperature in the process could vary an amount equal to 2%, and the measuring system would not respond at all. The indication or record of that temperature would appear as a straight line, whereas a considerable deviation would be taking place, and which might possibly be very detrimental to the process. Since the measuring system could not detect these variations, the controller could certainly not be expected to correct for them.

The effect of hysteresis in the measuring element would impart somewhat similar characteristics to the control obtainable.

If, in a temperature measuring and controlling system, the measuring system is such that its range covers only a very narrow portion of the possible variation in the process, the control obtainable is apt to be inadequate. This may be because necessary adjustments to the controller in order to obtain smooth control are such that only a very slight corrective action is obtainable as a result of the narrow band of measurement. In other words, the entire range of the controller may be utilized to produce only a fraction of the possible movement of the control valve. The result is that the controller is powerless to move the control valve further once it has reached one end of the measuring band.

Throttling control is generally obtainable if the measuring band extends beyond the range of variation of the process. In this case full control valve movement may be had, if necessary, in response to the variations.

The above discussion on wide band vs. narrow band measurement and its effect on control is very general and must necessarily be so at this point. The adjustments to the controller and the type of controller used have considerable effect when comparing wide band vs. narrow band measurement and effects. These points will be brought out later. It is sufficient to state, however, that the measuring system band or range should be great enough to cover all possible variations in the medium in order to provide adequate control effects.

Not all measuring devices are adaptable to control mechanisms. To be used in a controller, the measuring system must do work, and thus possess a given amount of power to do this work. It must develop sufficient power to do this work as well as measure the variable accurately. The work done in actuating the control mechanism must not be at the expense of the measurement, for a controller which cannot first measure accurately is worthless.

In some measuring systems it is not practical to obtain movement for the purpose of actuating a control mechanism. As

Information Sheet 2

an example, a glass U-tube containing a liquid such as mercury is
an excellent pressure measuring device, but it could not be easily
adapted to actuate a control mechanism. Modifications to the U-
tube principle are employed, such as in mercury actuated differential pressure motors, where a float rides on the mercury surface,
and the motion is obtained from the float movement as the mercury
level changes. This modification is so designed as to produce
sufficient power to indicate or record the measurement and to also
actuate the automatic control mechanism.

Other measuring systems which in themselves are not directly
adaptable to control mechanisms include galvanometers and rotameters.
Galvanometers are incorporated into controllers, but merely sense
variations. The force or power for indicating, recording and controlling is supplied from another source. This is also true
regarding rotameters when they are to record or control.

Glass stem thermometers and hydrometers are further examples
of measuring devices not generally suitable for attachment to
control mechanisms used on industrial processes. Low pressure
measuring systems such as draft gages are also unsuitable for
directly actuating control systems because of the low power developed. These must be supplemented by another actuating force when
it is desired to use them in conjunction with a control means.

Pressure and temperature systems of the Bourdon spring and
diaphragm types can be used in automatic controllers because they
have been designed to develop sufficient power for controlling
purposes without sacrificing accuracy of the measurement. Motion
actuated elements, such as floats, are readily adaptable to controllers as they are designed to produce power.

For best results in an automatic control system, the measuring
system should respond to variations of the process as quickly as
possible. In an automatic control circuit there must be a deviation
in the measuring system before any corrective action can be taken
by the control mechanism. If the measuring system is slow in responding to changes as they take place, there will be a delay in
the application of the correction by the controller. This means
that a further deviation is likely to take place before the process
feels any correction.

There are adjustments in most controllers whereby stable control
can be obtained in spite of slow response of the measuring system.
On the other hand, the effect of these adjustments show up as undesirable characteristics in the control obtainable when an upset
in the process takes place. It is, therefore, of prime importance
that the measuring system have a high speed of response, so that
the maxiumum good can be realized from the control system as a
whole.

Information Sheet 3   DEFINITION OF TERMS

Unfortunately the terms used in controller theory and application to industrial processes are not universal. As each manufacturer developed and improved his controllers, he found that names were not available to describe the various controller responses and process characteristics. Therefore, descriptive names were selected at random and often one manufacturer's selection did not agree with another's, even though they meant the same thing. Since the automatic control industry is relatively new, it has only been within the last few years that a need for a unified set of terms has been recognized. A set of proposed process control terms has been published in Volume 66, No. 3 of Mechanical Engineering, March 1944, but it seems likely that these definitions will be revised and supplemented considerably before they are widely accepted in this field.

Since rigorous technical definitions are hard to understand and are unnecessary to a text of this sort, an effort will be made to simplify the following definitions to make them more readily understandable.

Process

An operation which changes at least one physical or chemical characteristic of a material.

Unit Process

An arbitrary division of a process.

Controlled Variable

A quantity or condition which is measured and controlled by an automatic controller.

Control Agent

Material or process energy which affects the value of the controlled variable and whose flow is regulated by the final control element.

Automatic Controller

A mechanism which measures the value of a variable quantity or condition subject to change with time and operates to maintain it within limits.

Information Sheet 3

Self-Acting Controller

A controller which obtains the energy for operation of the final control element from the measuring element.

Air-Operated Controller

A controller which amplifies the power from the measuring element by using air or gas pressure to operate the final control element.

Direct-Acting Controller

A controller which increases the controlled air pressure as the value of the controlled variable increases.

Reverse-Acting Controller

A controller which decreases the controlled air pressure as the value of the controlled variable increases.

Control System

Those elements which, acting together, produce corrective action based on indications supplied by the measuring element.

Measuring Element

Those elements which are involved in measuring the changes of the controlled variable.

Primary Control Element

That part of the controller which causes the motion or variation of the measuring element to actuate the controller system.

Final Control Element

That portion of the controller system which directly varies a control agent.

Controller Response

The action obtained from a controller as a result of a change in the controlled variable.

On-and-Off Response

A controller response in which the final control element is moved immediately from one extreme to the other extreme of its stroke as a result of a change in the controlled variable.

Information Sheet 3

Proportional Response

A controller response which is proportional to the changes of a controlled variable.

Reset Response

A controller response whose rate of change is proportional to the deviation of the controlled variable.

Rate Response - Derivative Response

A controller response which is proportional to the rate of change of the controlled variable.

Throttling Range - Proportional Band

The range of values through which the controlled variable must vary to cause the final control element to move from one extreme to the other.

Reset Rate

The unit of measurement of reset response. The ratio between the rate of movement of the final control element due to reset response and that due to proportional response following a single action of the measuring element. Reset rate is usually expressed as 'repeats per minute .

Rate Time - Derivative Time

The unit of measurement of rate response. The time interval by which the final control element, actuated by rate response, anticipates a subsequent position due to proportional response.

Reset Time

The time for the reset system to approach equilibrium after an upset.

Set Point

That value of the controlled variable which it is desired to maintain.

Deviation

The difference at any instant between the value of the controlled variable and the set point.

Information Sheet 3

Control Point

The average value of the controlled variable which the controller actually maintains under steady load conditions.

Off-Set - Droop

The difference between the set point and the control point of a proportional controller. It is caused by a sustained load change.

Sensitivity

A unit of measurement of proportional response. The ratio of the movement of the final control element to the movement of the measuring element due to proportional response alone.

Hunting

Cyclic variations of the controlled variable due to the action of the controller.

Process Time Lag

The interval of time which elapses between a change in the final control element and its first effect on the measuring element. This is a process characteristic and is a major factor in determining controller adjustments.

Wander - Drift

Irregular variations in the controlled variable.

****

A more complete glossary of terms will be found in Appendix I of this monograph.

Information Sheet 4   BASIC CONTROL THEORY

In explaining the theory of automatic controls, it is well to consider that the trained operator could duplicate for a short period the results obtained with automatic controls. With this in mind, the four major control responses will be described:

        1. On-and-off response.
        2. Proportional response.
        3. Proportional plus reset response.
        4. Proportional plus rate response.

Each of these will be explained by describing the action of an operator who is duplicating the valve movements that would result from the use of the particular controller response.

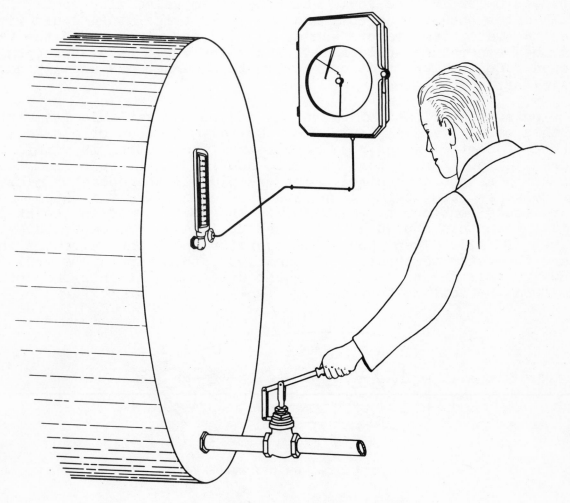

Fig. 2 - Manual Temperature Control

Assume that the operator will attempt to control the temperature of water in a tank at 190°F. by operating a valve that controls

Information Sheet 4

steam being supplied to a heating coil, as shown in Fig. 2. The
tank is equipped with a thermometer so that the operator can read
the water temperature and a recorder to show past performance.
There is a stream of cold water entering the tank and hot water
leaving the tank.

On-and-Off Response

In explaining this type of response, it is assumed that the
operator was told to control the water temperature in the tank at
190° by completely opening and completely closing the steam valve.
A constant rate of flow of water through the tank is also assumed.

The operator would watch the thermometer and when the temperature was below 190° he would hold the steam valve wide open. Steam
would enter the heating coil and the water temperature would rise.
When the water temperature was above 190°, he would close the valve,
and the temperature would fall. The valve would be either open or
closed. Controllers that operate in this manner are usually called
on-and-off controllers.

On some applications where the controlled variable (temperature
in this case) changes slowly when the valve is open or closed, this
method of control gives good results and the control is within
close limits. More often than not, hunting will result from the
use of this type of control. For example, if the operator closed
the valve as soon as the temperature reached 190°, the water temperature would continue to rise, due to the heat stored in the steam
coil. When this stored heat is used up, the water temperature
starts to fall. Even though the operator opens the valve the instant the water temperature reaches 190°, the temperature would continue to fall due to the time required to get heat into the coil
and from the coil to the water.

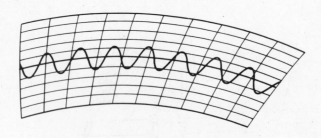

Fig. 3 - On-and-Off Response

The record produced by the recorder would be as shown in Fig. 3.
The effect of the repeated temperature cycles as illustrated by
this curve is known as hunting or cycling. It is not hard to
imagine that such control would be unsatisfactory in many cases.

Information Sheet 4

Proportional Response

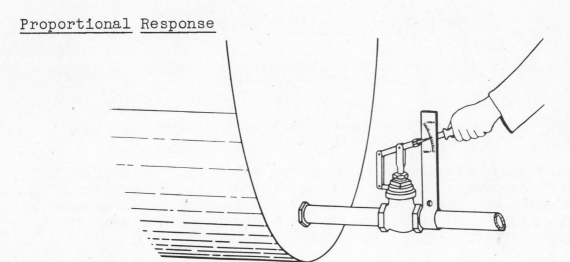

Fig. 4

In order to eliminate the hunting action that results from the use of on-and-off response, proportional response is used. To simulate this response it would be necessary to place a scale beside the valve handle, as shown in Fig. 4.

This scale will make it possible for the operator to tell at a glance the exact position of the valve. For the purpose of this explanation it is assumed that the valve will have to be half open in order to hold the water temperature at 190° with a constant rate of flow of water through the tank. It is also assumed that whenever the operator moves the valve he moves it exactly in proportion to the amount which the temperature deviates from 190°. It is also assumed that, if the water temperature should rise from 190° to 200°, the operator would close the valve. Likewise, if the water temperature should decrease from 190° to 180° the operator would open the valve. Thus this 20° change in water temperature would cause the operator to move the valve through its full travel from open to closed. For each degree change in temperature the operator would move the valve through 1/20 of its stroke.

In applying this system to increase the temperature of the water in the tank to 190° from a lower temperature, the operator will have the valve more than half open. Then, as the water temperature rises, he will slowly close the valve. When the temperature reaches 190° the valve will be half open but because of the heat already added, the temperature will continue to rise. When the temperature reaches 194° the valve will be only 6/20 open, which will not permit enough steam to enter the coil to maintain the temperature at 194°. Under this condition, the temperature will fall. As the temperature falls, the valve will be slowly opened so that at 190° the valve will be half open and at 188° it will be 12/20 open.

Information Sheet 4

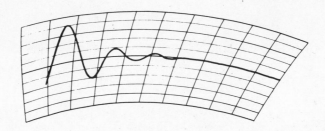

Fig. 5 - Proportional Response with Constant
Rate of Flow

This proportional movement of the valve will gradually damp
out the temperature oscillation and will result in stable control
at 190° with the valve half open. The record of this response is
shown in Fig. 5. Controllers that operate in this manner are
called proportional response controllers.

Proportional Plus Reset Response

Let us assume that after the operator had obtained stable control as described under proportional response, and as illustrated
in Fig. 5, the water flow, instead of remaining constant, decreases
in amount. This decrease in flow will mean that the temperature
will start to rise. If the operator is still acting to simulate
proportional response, he will gradually close the valve as the
temperature rises, closing it 1/20 of its full stroke for each
degree of temperature change.

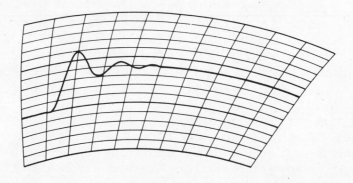

Fig. 6 - Proportional Response with Decrease
in Rate of Flow

The temperature will oscillate as it did before but at a higher
temperature, as shown in Fig. 6, due to the decreased flow of water.
We now have stable control at 194° with the control valve 6/20
open. The decreased flow of water has raised the water temperature 4°. This change in temperature has been accompanied by the
proportional change in valve position of 1/20 of full stroke for
each degree change in temperature. Although the operator has perfectly simulated proportional response, he is no longer controlling
the temperature at the desired 190°. Thus it is seen that

Information Sheet 4

proportional response alone is not enough to maintain a uniform temperature under conditions that require different valve positions for the same temperature.

The operator will now slowly close the valve still farther in order to reestablish the control at 190°. Let us assume that he slowly resets (closes) the valve until control is reestablished at 190°. When automatic control is used and the valve is reset in this manner, the control is called automatic reset.

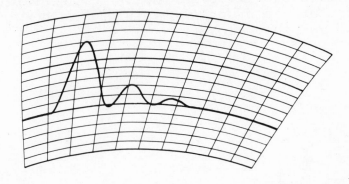

Fig. 7 - Proportional Plus Reset Response

By definition, automatic reset gives a continuing correction whose rate is proportional to the deviation. Therefore, if the operator is to perfectly simulate this response, he will have to reset the valve at a rate proportional to the change in temperature. For example, if the temperature changes 2° he will move the valve 2/20 of its travel due to proportional response, and he will also continue to reposition the valve at the same rate until the 190° temperature had been restored, as shown in Fig. 7.

Proportional Plus Rate Response

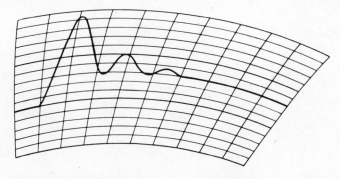

Fig. 8 - Proportional Response with Sudden
Decrease in Rate of Flow

Often a sudden large change in the rate of flow of the water will cause its temperature to rise high above or drop far below

Information Sheet 4

190°. If, when the temperature is increasing due to such a change in the rate of flow, the operator closes the steam valve according to proportional response alone, the record would be as shown in Fig. 8.

This condition of a sudden large decrease in the flow of water may be a part of a regularly recurring cycle due to batch process requirements. In this case, by knowing beforehand the size of batch or by watching the rate of temperature decrease, the operator may be able to move the valve farther and more rapidly when he sees that the temperature is dropping rapidly than he would according to proportional response alone.

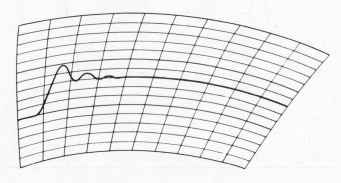

Fig. 9 - Proportional Plus Rate Response with
Sudden Decrease in Rate of Flow

Thus he would anticipate the rate at which the valve should be moved according to the rate of temperature deviation and thus stability of control would be restored in less time but not at the desired temperature since reset response is not used. See Fig. 9. The response of a system in which the valve is moved an amount proportional to the temperature deviation, plus an added amount depending on the rate of that deviation, is called proportional plus rate response.

Combinations of proportional, reset and rate responses may be used. Reset response and rate response must always be used in combination with proportional response. A combination of all three of these responses may also be used.

Information Sheet 4

Fig. 10 shows an
actual chart record
of an automatic tem-
perature controller
with proportional
plus reset response
when applied to the
temperature regula-
tion of a shredder
used in the rayon
textiles industry.
The peaks on the curve
indicate the time be-
tween batches when the
shredder is not in
operation.

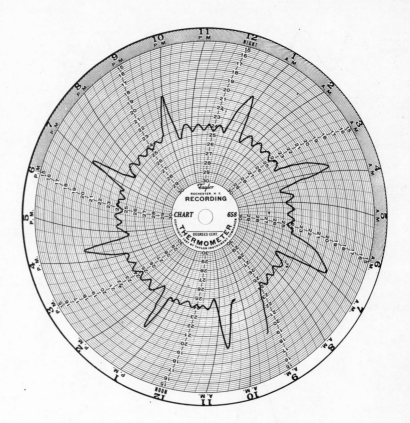

Fig. 10

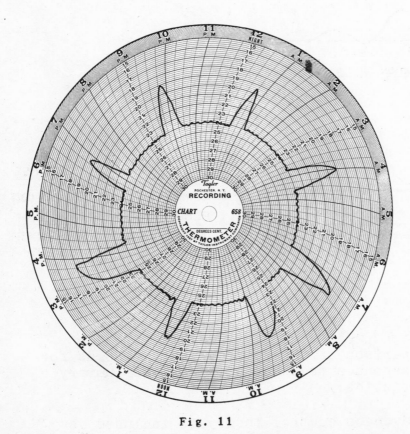

Fig. 11 shows the chart
record for the same
installation when rate
response has been added.

Fig. 11

Information Sheet 4

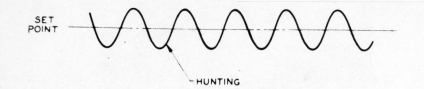

ON-OFF RESPONSE

CHARACTERIZED BY HUNTING ACTION.

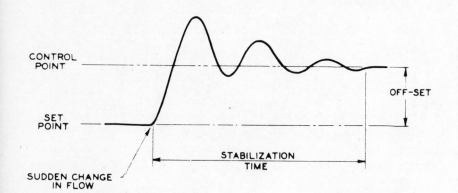

PROPORTIONAL RESPONSE

ELIMINATES HUNTING ACTION.

INTRODUCES OFF-SET EXCEPT WHEN THERE IS A CONSTANT RATE OF FLOW.

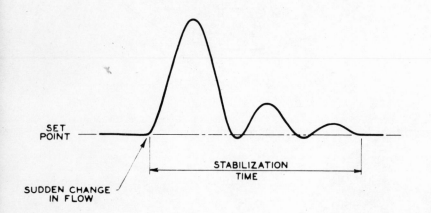

RESET RESPONSE

ELIMINATES HUNTING ACTION.

ELIMINATES OFF-SET.

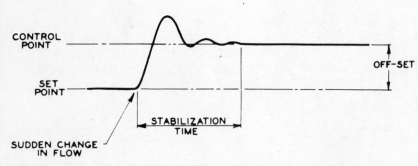

RATE (PRE-ACT) RESPONSE

ELIMINATES HUNTING ACTION.

REDUCES STABILIZATION TIME.

INTRODUCES OFF-SET EXCEPT WHEN THERE IS A CONSTANT RATE OF FLOW.

Fig. 12

Fig. 12 gives a comparison of theoretical chart records for the four major control responses together with a brief summary of their important characteristics.

An explanation of advanced control theory is included as Appendix II of this monograph.

Information Sheet 5   SIMPLE CONTROLLERS

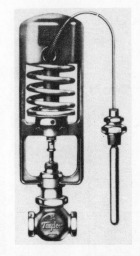

Courtesy of Taylor Instrument Companies

Probably the best known use of automatic controls is in the regulating of oil burners, automatic stokers and gas burning furnaces for heating modern dwellings and apartments.

The basic principles of control theory can be illustrated by thinking in terms of controlling the temperature of your own home. If your home is equipped with a hand-fired coal furnace, an uncomfortable feeling of cold on a winter day may tell you that the temperature of your living room is falling. You will then open the furnace draft, clean the grate and apply more coal. There will be a time delay, however, between the time at which you noticed the lowered temperature in the room and the time at which the furnace has corrected the difficulty. For, if the outdoor temperature is dropping, the temperature of the room may continue to drop for several minutes after you have refueled the furnace. Also, if the temperature of the room has lowered but one or two degrees, it will take a considerable volume of heated air to mix with the larger volume of air already in the room before there is any noticeable change of temperature. Such a process is not instantaneous and it is apparent that maintaining a constant temperature will depend upon factors such as the outdoor temperature, the size of the room, the insulation of the walls, the capacity of the heating system, and the rate at which the heating system responds to an added demand for heat.

If the above room were equipped with a controller sensitive to temperature changes of extremely small values, a constant temperature could not be maintained without first overcoming these other difficulties.

The example above serves to illustrate how temperature deviations due to inherent characteristics of a process may be mistaken for inadequacies of the controlling device. When control trouble develops, it is easy to assume that the trouble is caused by failure of the control mechanism. A careful study of the problem may reveal a combination of causes including instrument adjustments and process difficulties.

To better understand the operation and the limitations of various types of controllers, let us examine the construction and observe typical installation diagrams of several simple control mechanisms.

Fig. 13 shows the construction of a self-acting temperature controller, the valve shown in the figure is held open by means of the compression-type spring. Notice the construction of the

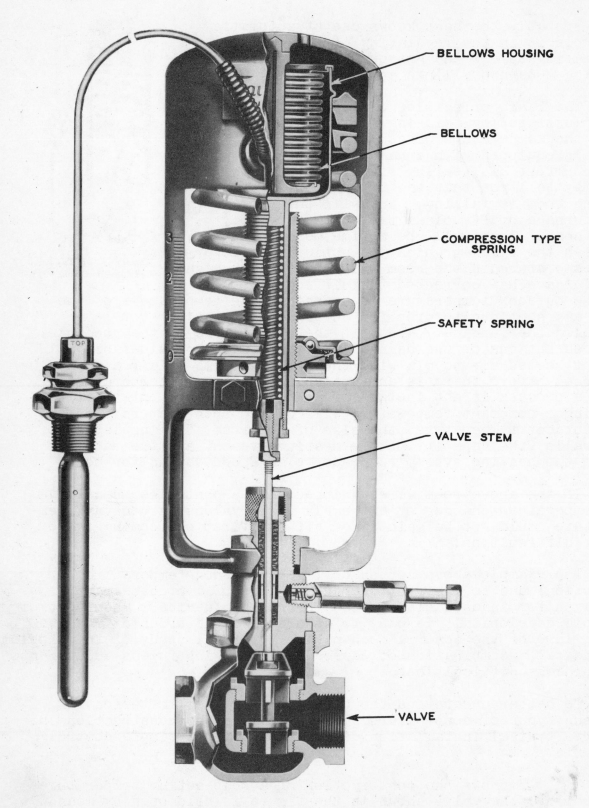

Fig. 13 - Self-Acting Temperature Controller
Courtesy of Taylor Instrument Companies

Information Sheet 5

bellows unit. Liquid having a suitable vapor pressure is sealed within the system and exerts pressure between the bellows housing and the outside of the bellows. The upward force of the compression spring tends to hold the valve open against the force of the vapor pressure which tends to close the valve. Hence, the position of the valve may be adjusted by regulating the spring tension. An increase of temperature at the bulb increases the vapor pressure within the system. This forces the valve stem downward, compressing the bellows and closing the valve. The temperature to which the controller is set may be regulated by turning the nut upon which the compression type spring rests.

The safety spring shown in Fig. 13 protects the bellows from extreme pressures. When the bulb is subjected to temperatures beyond the range of the system the safety spring permits the expansion needed to reduce the pressure within the bellows and thus prevents its rupture or distortion. To further illustrate this we might assume an extreme case in which the bulb temperature was high enough to evaporate all of the liquid within the bulb. There would be no damage to the system if the safety spring could be made to absorb the expansion due to this evaporation.

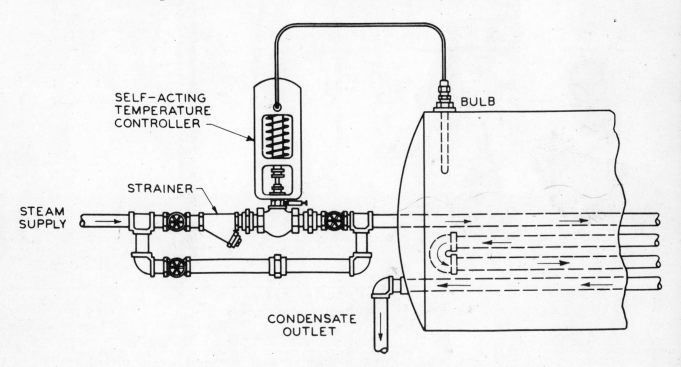

Fig. 14 - Installation of a Self-Acting Temperature Controller
Courtesy of Taylor Instrument Companies

Fig. 14 shows an installation of this controller when used to regulate the temperature of a hot water tank.

Information Sheet 5

The use of this controller is limited to valve sizes of two inches or less and to installations which do not require a wide throttling range. Its throttling range depends on the temperature range and the size of the valve but will generally fall within 10° and 20°F.

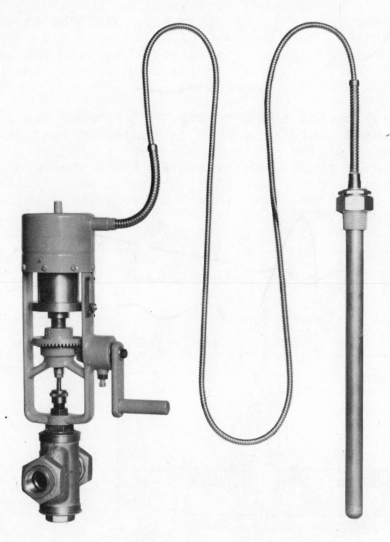

Fig. 15 - Self-Acting Regulator
Courtesy of Fulton Sylphon Company

Fig. 15 shows a self-acting temperature regulator which is provided with a crank adjustment so that any spring pressure and thus any temperature setting within the range of the regulator can be conveniently selected.

Information Sheet 5

Pressure Balanced Air or Gas Regulator

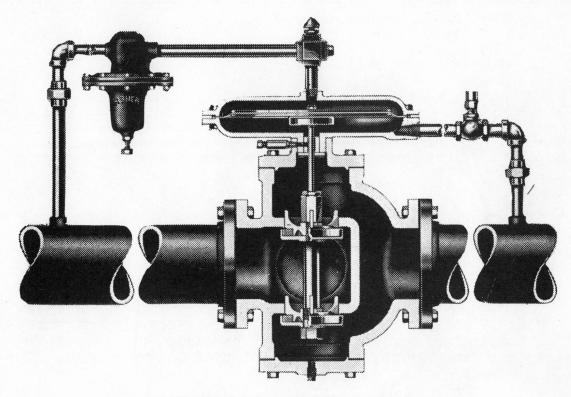

Fig. 16 - Pressure Balanced Air or Gas Regulator
Courtesy of Fisher Governor Company

Fig. 16 is a cut-away view of a pressure balanced air or gas regulator. Air or gas pressure from a high pressure line is admitted to the large pipe at the left of the figure. A short section of small diameter pipe carries this pressure to a pressure reducing regulator. From this point the reduced pressure is conducted to the top of the diaphragm chamber.

A small pipe connects the lower diaphragm chamber to the reduced pressure line.

With this type of regulator, the degree of opening of the control valve is regulated by the balance of pressure between the constant reduced pressure value admitted above the diaphragm and the varying output pressure admitted below the diaphragm.

Thus a drop of pressure in the output line will cause an increase in the amount of valve opening. This will then increase the pressure in the output line until the pressures above and

Information Sheet 5

below the diaphragm are equal, causing the system to reach equilibrium at a new point of increased valve opening.

Similarly, an increase of output pressure will cause a further
closing of the valve and the pressures will equalize with the valve
in a new position of decreased opening.

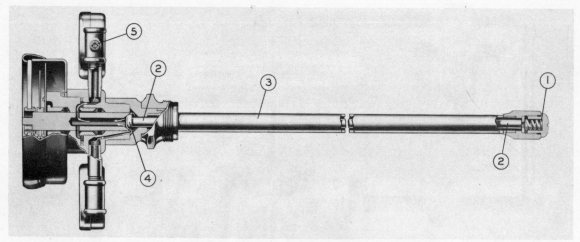

Fig. 17 - Expansion Stem Temperature Controller
Courtesy of Taylor Instrument Companies

Fig. 17 shows a cut-away view of an air-operated direct-
acting temperature controller. The controller operates on the
principle of the varying expansion rates of unlike metals.

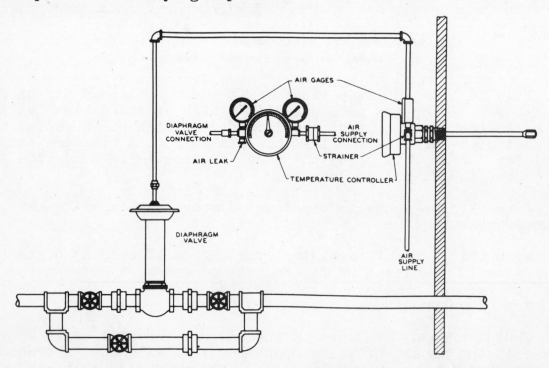

Fig. 18 - Installation of the Expansion Stem
Temperature Controller
Courtesy of Taylor Instrument Companies

Information Sheet 5

The outer housing or expanding stem 3 is placed in contact with the heated media. An inner rod, or non-expanding stem 2, terminates in valve disc 4 at one end while spring 1 at the opposite end keeps the rod in contact with expanding stem 3.

When the liquid within the tank, Fig. 18, becomes sufficiently heated, expanding stem 3, Fig.17, will expand sufficiently to release the pressure of bevel disc 4 from its seat. Sufficient air pressure will then pass through the valve to overcome the effect of air leak screw 5 and close the diaphragm valve which stops the flow of the heated liquid to the tank. Air leak screw 5 may be adjusted to regulate the controller sensitivity. Closing the air leak will increase the sensitivity which thus may be varied from 3° to 10°F. If the temperature of the tank drops so that disc 4 is again seated, the air pressure will bleed from the diaphragm causing the valve to admit more of the heated liquid. The control point is adjusted by moving the indicator hand on the large dial. This moves the valve seat towards or away from non-expanding stem 2.

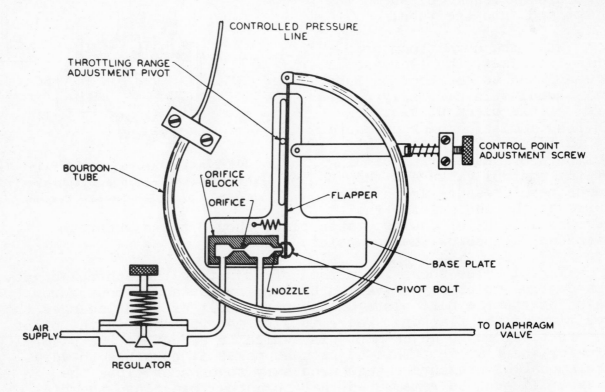

Fig. 19 - Schematic Diagram of a Pilot Type Pressure Controller
Courtesy of Fisher Governor Company

Fig. 19 is a schematic diagram of a pilot type air-operated automatic pressure controller used to maintain a constant pressure in the downstream or outlet line from a diaphragm valve. The pilot valve assembly may be remotely mounted on a panel board, or it may be an integral part of the diaphragm assembly of the main control valve, as shown in Fig. 20.

Information Sheet 5

Assuming that the controller is to maintain a constant
downstream pressure or reduced
pressure in a pipe line as in
Fig. 20, the operation is as
follows: Auxiliary air pressure
enters the pilot, Fig. 19,
through a regulator and passes
into the orifice block through
the fixed orifice to the bleed
nozzle. The opening at that
nozzle is controlled by the
flapper, which in turn is actuated by the movement of the
Bourdon tube. The free end of
the Bourdon tube moves in accordance with the variations in
the downstream or controlled
pressure, which is piped to the
pilot and into the tube.

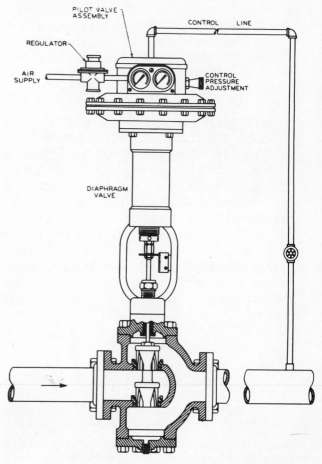

When the downstream pres-
sure increases, the increase is
transmitted to the Bourdon tube.
This results in partially closing off the bleed nozzle,
thereby admitting back pressure
to the diaphragm valve. This
action provides partial closing
of the control valve and the
downstream pressure again returns to the set point. The

Fig. 20 - Installation of the Pilot Type
Pressure Controller on a Diaphragm Valve
Courtesy of Fisher Governor Company.

reverse action, of course, takes place should the downstream
pressure fall below the set point.

Fig. 19 also shows the method of adjusting the control point.
The control point may be varied by turning the adjustment screw
which pivots the base plate on the pivot bolt and thus changes the
position of the flapper. There is also incorporated in the pilot
a throttling range adjustment pin, which in effect is the pivot
pin for the flapper. This adjustment makes it possible to vary
the amount of pressure change necessary to open or close the
valve. It must be remembered that in actual practice, the diaphragm valve is seldom completely closed or completely open. It
usually is a throttling valve and floats, so to speak, between
those two points. The throttling range of this pilot is from 1
to 75% of the Bourdon tube range.

These pilots can be changed from direct-acting to reverse-
acting, and can be used with various types of direct or reverse-
acting diaphragm control valves.

Information Sheet 5

Fig. 22 shows how the pressure controller shown in Fig. 21 may be used to regulate the pressure maintained by a control valve. To set the instrument at a given pressure, the adjusting knob, which operates the control setting cam is turned until the desired pressure is indicated by the gage at the left. The right-hand gage indicates the diaphragm valve pressure. Fig. 22 also shows how the controller operates. Air pressure admitted at the top of the figure passes through an adjustable orifice to lines leading to a diaphragm valve, a pressure gage and a pilot nozzle. A movable control arm placed near the nozzle varies the air flow from the nozzle whenever the controlled pressure is changed.

The pilot which controls the pilot nozzle openings rests on the control arm which is actuated by the Bourdon tube. The Bourdon tube in turn is actuated by the controlled pressure. The control arm is fastened to the movable end of the Bourdon tube by means of a pivot pin. The amount of movement of the pilot may be increased or decreased by moving the adjustable pivot to the left or to the right.

As the controlled pressure increases, the control arm is moved upward against the nozzle pilot and air bleeds freely from the nozzle. Hence, no back pressure is exerted against the diaphragm valve which remains closed. As the controlled pressure is reduced, the pilot is lowered by the Bourdon tube until the nozzle is partially closed. The back pressure in the line leading to the diaphragm valve is then increased till a point is reached at which the diaphragm valve partially opens to admit more pressure to the line.

Fig. 21 - A Pressure Controller
Courtesy of Mason-Neilan Regulator Co.

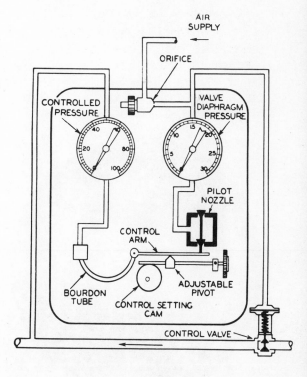

Fig. 22 - Schematic Diagram of the Pressure Controller
Courtesy of Mason-Neilan Regulator Co.

Information Sheet 5

The amount of pressure admitted depends upon the positioning of the diaphragm valve, which in turn depends upon the setting of the cam. Turning this cam will raise or lower the right end of the control arm. To raise this end will decrease the controlled pressure which is necessary to close the diaphragm valve, while to lower it will increase the controlled pressure which is necessary to open the valve.

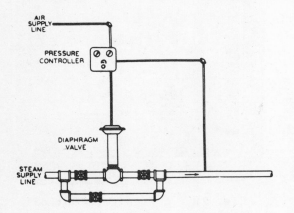

Fig. 23 - Installation of the
Pressure Controller

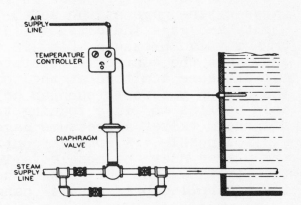

Fig. 24 - Installation of the
Temperature Controller

Courtesy of Mason-Neilan Regulator Company

Controllers of this type are available for either temperature or pressure installations. Fig. 23 shows an installation in which a pressure controller of this type is used to regulate the pressure in a steam line. Fig. 24 shows an installation in which a temperature controller of this type is used to regulate the temperature of a liquid in a tank.

Fig. 25 - A Temperature Controller

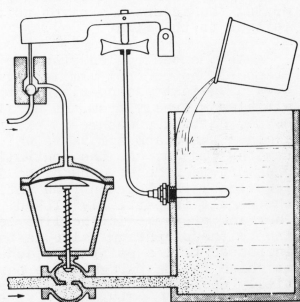

Fig. 26 - Operation of the Temperature
Controller

Courtesy of C.J. Tagliabue Manufacturing Company

Information Sheet 5

  Fig. 26 illustrates the operation of the temperature controller shown in Fig. 25. If the controller is set to maintain a specified temperature, cooling the bulb of the temperature sensitive element, as shown in the figure, will produce a contraction of the fluid within the system and deflate the capsular chamber. This lowers the lever which forces the ball against its lower seat, cutting off the air supply and allowing air to bleed from the chamber of the diaphragm valve. Spring pressure then opens the valve to admit more of the heated fluid.

  Increasing the temperature of the bulb will inflate the capsular chamber, allowing the ball to rise to its upper seat. This admits pressure to the diaphragm valve which begins to close, reducing the amount of heated fluid admitted.

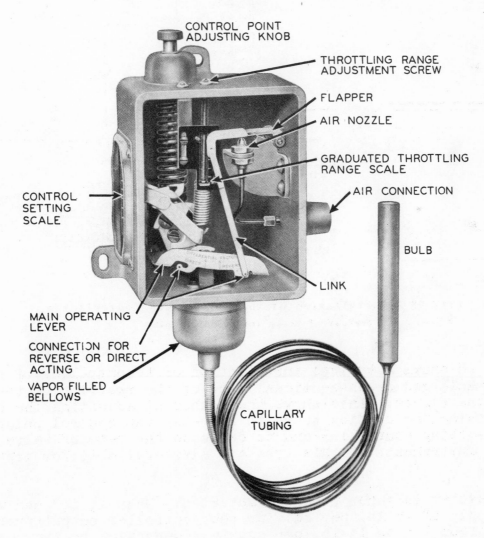

Fig. 27 - A Temperature Controller
Courtesy of Brown Instrument Company

Information Sheet 5

Fig. 27 shows a simple temperature controller in which the position of the flapper is regulated by means of a bellows which is attached to a suitable linkage. Both the control point and the throttling range of the instrument may be adjusted from outside the case. The throttling range is adjustable from 1 to 10% of the temperature range.

The main operating lever is pivoted at the center and the controller may be changed from reverse to direct-acting by changing the link from the right to the left side of the lever.

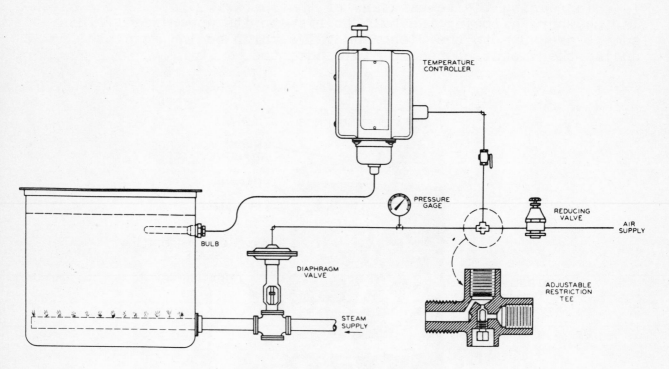

Fig. 28 - Installation of the Temperature Controller
Courtesy of Brown Instrument Company

Fig. 28 shows a typical installation of a controller of this type. An enlarged cross-sectional view of the restriction tee is shown in the figure. This shows the method of adjusting the orifice. Closing the orifice tends to increase the control point of a reverse-acting controller and to decrease the rate of valve closing. Instruments of this type are also available for pressure control.

The system is vapor pressure actuated. When it is used with an air supply of 15 lb. per sq. in. the controller output pressure will vary from 1.5 to 13 lb. per sq. in., depending on the position of the baffle.

Information Sheet 5

The control point is adjusted by turning the adjusting knob, Fig. 27, at the top of the controller. The throttling range is adjusted by turning the adjusting screw on the top of the case.

It should be noted here that while the simple controllers described above are well adapted to a large number of industrial uses most of them are limited in their throttling range, some do not provide throttling range adjustment or sufficient sensitivity adjustment. None of them have reset or rate response and none of them provide direct set features. A direct set instrument is one in which a pointer is set directly at the set point on the scale or chart of the instrument. Instruments which provide all of these features are described in Information Sheet 7.

An understanding of the simple mechanisms described in this unit is desirable, however, because many of the same operating principles and mechanisms are used in the more complex controllers.

Information Sheet 6   BASIC CONTROLLER MECHANISMS

In order to completely understand automatic controllers and automatic control systems, it is necessary to understand the elements which are used to produce the various control effects. These basic elements have the same relation to the finished controller that bricks, stone and lumber have to a completed building. While all the instrument designers seem to use these same basic elements in making up their controllers, the finished instruments differ considerably in their performance and ease of adjustment.

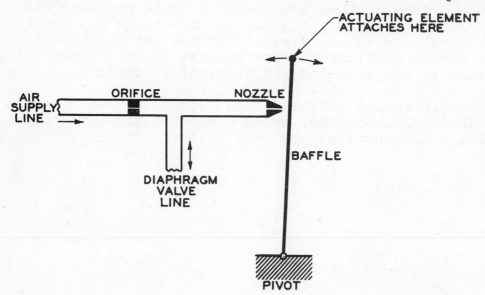

.Fig. 29 - Schematic Diagram of Orifice, Nozzle and Baffle Combination

The orifice, nozzle and baffle combination exists in almost all air-operated controllers. A constant air supply is fed to a small orifice which in turn is connected to a nozzle of somewhat larger diameter. See Fig. 29. When a baffle, sometimes called a flapper, moves closer to the nozzle, the pressure in the line between the orifice and the nozzle rises. This rise in pressure may be used to operate a diaphragm valve. When the baffle leaves the nozzle the pressure in this line falls, since the restriction at the nozzle is less than that at the orifice. A bellows or a Bourdon tube usually supplies the force used to move the baffle against the pressure of the air stream issuing from the nozzle in order to back up the pressure in that line. The force required is directly proportional to the line pressure as well as to the cross-sectional area of the nozzle. For example, a nozzle having a diameter of .050" will produce a force against the baffle four times as great as a nozzle with a diameter of .025" under the same conditions. Since the baffle is usually moved by the measuring element which has a relatively low power output, it is desirable to keep the force against the baffle at a minimum, thereby restraining its movement as little as possible. For this reason the nozzle diameter is usually reduced to the lowest practical value.

Information Sheet 6

As the nozzle diameter is reduced, the orifice diameter which is used with it must be reduced also. For example, if an orifice having a diameter of .025" were used with a nozzle of the same diameter, and an air supply of 20 psi, the minimum pressure in the line between the orifice and the nozzle would be in the neighborhood of 10 psi, with the nozzle wide open. Therefore, the maximum variation possible in this line under these conditions would be 10 psi, that is, from 10 to 20 psi. This pressure variation might not be adequate. On the other hand, if an orifice having a diameter of .010" were used with a nozzle having a diameter of .025", the pressure in the line between the orifice and the nozzle would be in the neighborhood of 1 psi with the nozzle wide open. When the nozzle is closed under these conditions, a pressure variation of about 19 psi can be obtained. This is a much more satisfactory system.

As the orifice and the nozzle are made smaller, other difficulties are encountered. In the field, one seldom finds perfectly clean air for controller operation. As the orifice and nozzle are reduced in size, the danger of plugging and subsequent controller failure are increased. Therefore, a reasonable lower limit is reached. Nozzle diameters are seldom less than .020" and rarely exceed .040". The diameter of the orifice is usually from 1/3 to 1/2 that of the nozzle, and when restrictions greater than that of a .010" orifice are required, it is customary to substitute a tube or capillary of about this same diameter. Naturally, a tube offers a greater restriction to flow than an orifice of the same diameter.

Since the orifice and nozzle combination are bleeding air continuously in a controller, their small size is a good feature in that it reduces the air consumption. On the other hand, whenever the volume of the line between the orifice and the nozzle is increased, for example, by the addition of a bellows or diaphragm, it takes a long time to inflate and deflate these volumes. This results in a slow response which is often undesirable. Therefore, it has become customary to limit the volume in this system to a relatively small value in most control systems, and utilize an air relay valve to amplify the air volume when large capacities must be inflated and deflated. In most cases air relay valves amplify pressure as well as volume, and the ratio of the change in output pressure to the change in input pressure through the relay valve is called its 'amplification factor' or 'gain'. Relay valves may be either direct or reverse-acting. In a direct-acting valve, an increase in the input pressure results in an increase in the output pressure. The opposite is true in a reverse-acting valve.

There are many designs of relay valves, but all of them seem to fall into two general classes: namely, continuous bleed types and non-bleed types.

Information Sheet 6

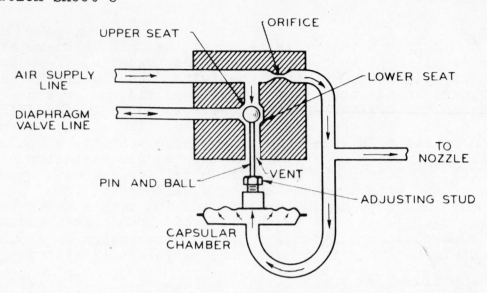

Fig. 30 - Schematic Diagram of a Continuous Bleed
Reverse-Acting Relay Valve
Courtesy of Taylor Instrument Companies

Fig. 30 is a schematic diagram of a continuous bleed reverse-acting relay valve. The nozzle back pressure enters the capsular chamber raising the pin and ball. When the pressure in the capsular chamber is low, the ball rests against the lower seat and the air flows directly from the supply line to the diaphragm valve line. When the pressure in the capsular chamber is high, the ball is forced against the upper seat allowing the air pressure from the diaphragm valve line to escape through the vent. For all intermediate pressures in the capsular chamber, the ball assumes a position somewhere between its two extreme positions so that air is continuously bleeding from the supply line to the diaphragm valve line and the vent. Thus the pressure in the diaphragm valve line depends upon the position of the ball which in turn depends upon the position of the capsular chamber and its internal pressure. This valve is called the 'continuous bleed type' since in all throttling positions (not on or off) the valve utilizes air.

In a valve of this type it is important that the air consumption be kept at a minimum so that the cost of operating the controller will not be excessive. For that reason the ball travel is never greater than .010". With a 20 psi air supply, the air consumption of a valve of this type is likely to be around 0.5 cu. ft. per min. when the ball is in its middle position. The air consumption decreases as the ball approaches either the upper or the lower seat. As the travel of the ball is increased, or as its diameter is increased, the air consumption increases, but designs in which the consumption exceeds 1 cu. ft. per min. are not generally recommended.

Information Sheet 6

The operating range of this relay is that range of pressure in the capsular chamber which will cause the output pressure to vary from zero to its maximum value. If the capsular chamber is made large and flexible, the relay valve becomes more sensitive, and its gain is high. Then only a very small pressure change is required in the capsular chamber to produce the full output pressure. In order to reduce the back pressure requirements from the orifice, nozzle and baffle combination, a relay valve with a relatively high gain is desirable. Most existing air relay valves have a gain between 5 and 20.

The operating pressure of most relay valves is adjusted by regulating the effective length of the valve stem. The operating pressure of this relay valve is regulated by turning the adjusting stud. When the stud is raised, a lower back pressure in the capsular chamber will move the ball through its entire length of stroke. When the stud is lowered, a higher back pressure is required to move the ball through its entire stroke. Note that this stud adjustment simply shifts the operating range but does not lengthen or shorten it. In the orifice, nozzle and baffle combination it is considerably more difficult to back up pressures approaching 20 psi with a 20 psi air supply than to back up pressures less than 10 psi. In other words, low pressures may be obtained in the line between the orifice and nozzle without sealing off the nozzle too tightly.

In order to make it unnecessary to provide an air-tight seal between the baffle and nozzle, relay valves are generally designed to operate on low nozzle back pressures. For example, this particular relay valve was designed to operate on back pressures varying between 2 and 4 psi with an air supply of 20 psi. Thus it is only necessary to back up 4 psi in the capsular chamber, to cause the output pressure from this relay valve to diminish to zero. Since the ball is on the lower seat and the diaphragm valve line pressure is 20 psi, when the capsular chamber pressure is 2 psi, the gain of this relay valve is minus 10. The valve is reverse-acting. Since the use of the relay valve of this type reduces the back pressure requirement at the nozzle, the force requirements at the baffle are reduced, and another advantage is gained. Although a maximum of 4 psi nozzle back pressure is required to operate this relay valve, it is customary to provide 6 to 8 psi to insure operation under all conditions.

Information Sheet 6

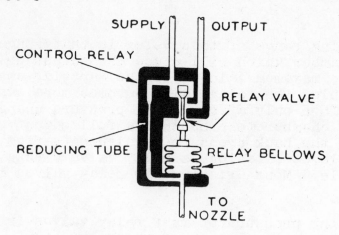

SUPPLY   OUTPUT

CONTROL RELAY

RELAY VALVE

REDUCING TUBE   RELAY BELLOWS

TO
NOZZLE

Fig. 31 - Schematic Diagram of a Continuous Bleed
Direct-Acting Relay Valve
Courtesy of Foxboro Company

Fig. 31 is a schematic diagram of a bellows operated continuous bleed relay valve. This relay valve is direct-acting, hence a clogged reducing tube would have the same effect on the system as failure of the air supply.

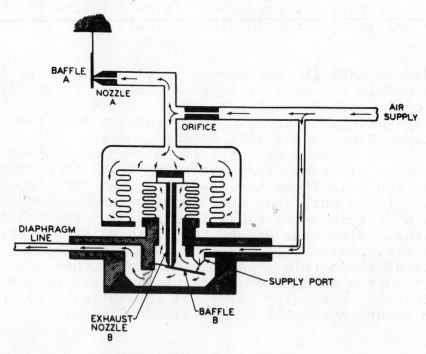

BAFFLE
A

NOZZLE
A

AIR
SUPPLY

ORIFICE

DIAPHRAGM
LINE

SUPPLY PORT

EXHAUST
NOZZLE
B

BAFFLE
B

Fig. 32 - Schematic Diagram of a Non-Bleed Type Relay
Valve with Nozzle Closed
Courtesy of Brown Instrument Company

Figs. 32 and 33 illustrate the operation of a typical non-bleed relay valve. With the baffle against the nozzle as shown in Fig. 32, back pressure behind nozzle A acts upon the outside of the

Information Sheet 6

large outer bellows. As this pressure increases, the large bellows forces exhaust nozzle B downward against baffle B, forcing open the supply port and admitting the full pressure of the air supply to the diaphragm valve line. This causes the pressure to increase within the small inner bellows until the upward force is greater than the downward force of the large outer bellows and causes the inner bellows to move upward carrying exhaust nozzle B with it and allowing baffle B to close the supply port. In this condition air is not being consumed by the relay valve.

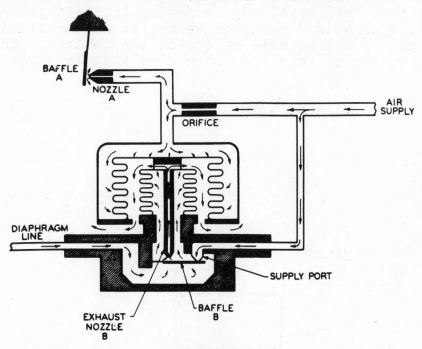

Fig. 33 - Schematic Diagram of the Non-Bleed Relay
Valve with Nozzle Open
Courtesy of Brown Instrument Company

As baffle A moves away from the nozzle, Fig. 33, the back pressure behind the nozzle diminishes and the larger outer bellows moves upward, carrying with it exhaust nozzle B. Air bleeds from the diaphragm valve line through exhaust nozzle B to the atmosphere, as indicated by the arrows, and the pressure is reduced within the small inner bellows. This in turn restores the exhaust nozzle to its original position and the air is neither supplied to nor exhausted from the relay valve. The pressure within the small inner bellows is the output from the relay valve and it bears a definite relationship to the nozzle back pressure which is the input to this relay valve. The gain of this relay valve is determined primarily by the ratio of the effective areas of the two bellows. If the large bellows has an area five times that of the smaller bellows, a pressure change of 1 psi in the nozzle back pressure will cause an output pressure change of 5 psi. Since an increase in the nozzle back pressure results in an increase in the output pressure, this valve is direct-acting.

Information Sheet 6

Non-bleed relay valves have the advantage of using less air, but they also possess a dead spot. To illustrate this, let us assume that the nozzle back pressure has increased just enough to close the exhaust nozzle in the relay valve, and yet this exhaust nozzle does not support any of the force exerted on the baffle which is required to close the supply nozzle. Now as the nozzle back pressure increases, it must first transfer this force from the supply port to the exhaust nozzle before it can open the supply port. This results in a dead spot which does not seem to be avoidable in a relay valve of this type. By designing the unit properly, the dead spot in a non-bleed relay valve may be made sufficiently small so that it has no appreciable effect on the control. This is the reason that valves of this type have a relatively large actuating bellows.

Mechanical Sensitivity Adjustment

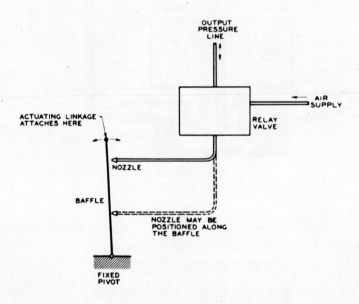

Fig. 34 - A Method of Obtaining Mechanical
Sensitivity Adjustment

From the theory which was developed in Information Sheet 4, it is apparent that some means should be provided in an automatic controller for adjusting the magnitude of its proportional response. In other words, provision must be made in the controller to adjust the ratio between its output and its input. In automatic controllers this is most often called sensitivity adjustment and in the air-operated type controllers it is measured in pounds per square inch per unit change in the input to the controller. There are two general methods of adjusting the sensitivity in a controller; one is wholly mechanical and the other is a combination of a mechanical and a pneumatic system.

Information Sheet 6

A mechanical method of adjusting the sensitivity of a controller is illustrated by Fig. 34. Motion from a Bourdon tube, manometer or other actuating element, operates a baffle which opens and closes a nozzle. The nozzle back pressure operates a relay valve which varies the pressure to a diaphragm valve or other final control element. In this particular system the location of the nozzle may be varied along the baffle by a manual operation so that the sensitivity of the controller can be varied. When the nozzle is a long way from the fixed pivot, the controller sensitivity will be high, since a large output pressure change will be caused by a very small motion of the measuring element. On the other hand, when the nozzle is close to the fixed pivot, a much smaller output pressure change results from this same motion of the measuring element and the sensitivity is lower. Now there are many variations of this lever arrangement, but in any of these where the motion of the baffle at the nozzle is reduced by a simple lever arrangement, it is a mechanical sensitivity reduction or adjustment.

From a study of this system and other lever systems belonging to this class, it will be apparent that more force is required from the measuring element to open and close the nozzle enough to actuate the relay valve when it is in its upper or high sensitivity position. Since only a limited power is available from the measuring element, there is a high limit to the sensitivity which can be obtained from any instrument. This depends upon a number of factors which may be easily tabulated. Higher mechanical sensitivities may be obtained from controllers which have:

1. Powerful measuring elements
2. Small diameter nozzles
3. Low nozzle back pressure requirements

In all instrument designs, compromises are necessary, but it may be seen that an added advantage is gained when a design utilizes a small nozzle and a relay valve with a high gain since this reduces the nozzle back pressure requirement.

In Fig. 34 as the nozzle is moved towards the fixed pivot and the sensitivity is lowered, another limitation is encountered. A certain amount of friction or dead spot in the linkage or in the relay valve of the controller is unavoidable. In well-designed relay valves which are carefully made, this may be small. However, in most relay valves these effects are appreciable and must be considered in the instrument design. In order to illustrate our point, let us take a typical relay valve which might have a dead spot in its output pressure of 0.5 psi. In other words, the difference between the two values of the output pressure as the pressure in the capsular chamber approaches a given value from opposite directions is 0.5 psi. If the gain in the relay valve is 10, this dead spot or 'hysteresis' would correspond to a pressure change of 0.05 psi in the capsular chamber. Now, if the nozzle

Information Sheet 6

were located at a high sensitivity position so that only 0.05°F.
were necessary to produce a motion of the baffle sufficient to
create a pressure change of 0.05 psi, this dead spot might be im-
perceptible and for this reason be negligible on the average temperature control application. On the other hand, if the nozzle
were located at a low sensitivity position near the fixed pivot so
that a temperature change of possibly 5 degrees were necessary to
overcome this hysteresis or dead spot, it would become apparent
and would be objectionable on most control problems. Thus it can
be seen that as the sensitivity of the controller is lowered by the
mechanical adjustment of the nozzle, or by any other purely mechanical system, a point is finally reached where the control is not
acceptable. Thus there is a lower limit on the mechanical sensitivity adjustment which depends primarily on the characteristics
of the relay valve and the linkage.

Pneumatic Sensitivity Adjustment

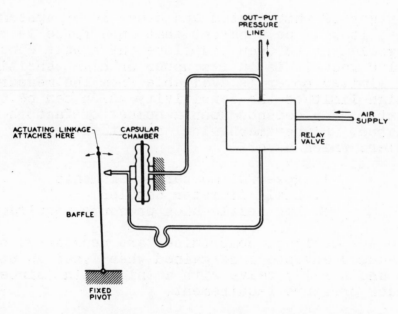

Fig. 35 - A Method of Obtaining Pneumatic
Sensitivity Adjustment

The combined mechanical and pneumatic method of adjusting the
sensitivity is usually spoken of as 'pneumatic sensitivity reduction'.
Fig. 35 illustrates a simplified method of accomplishing this. In
this figure the nozzle is mounted on a capsular chamber, but is not
connected to it pneumatically. The nozzle is connected to the
capsular chamber of the relay valve through a flexible tube. The
capsular chamber on which the nozzle is mounted is connected to the
output pressure line from the relay valve. The relay valve is
reverse-acting, so its output pressure decreases as the back
pressure from the nozzle increases.

Information Sheet 6

When the baffle is away from the nozzle, the nozzle back pressure is low, and the output pressure from the relay valve is high. The capsular chamber behind the nozzle is expanded and the nozzle is pushed to the left. As the baffle approaches the nozzle, the back pressure increases and the output pressure from the relay valve starts to diminish. This starts to deflate the capsular chamber behind the nozzle and the nozzle moves to the right. Thus the baffle must move through a much greater distance to close the nozzle and operate the relay valve than it would if the capsular chamber were omitted. Since the baffle must move farther, the measuring element must move farther in order to produce a given output pressure and the sensitivity of the controller is lowered. Since this sensitivity lowering is accomplished pneumatically, it is called pneumatic sensitivity reduction.

In order to realize an advantage obtained by pneumatic sensitivity reduction, let us assume that a capsular chamber has been selected which will move the nozzle so that 100 times the normal baffle motion is required to close the nozzle. If the original sensitivity (without the capsular chamber) were such that $0.05^\circ F$. were necessary to produce sufficient baffle movement to change the output pressure 0.5 psi, now it would require 100 times that to produce this same output pressure change. Under these conditions the sensitivity is identical with the assumed low sensitivity mentioned in discussing Fig. 34, namely $5^\circ F$. are required to produce an output pressure change of 0.5 psi. Now, however, if the output pressure from the relay valve fails to change due to its 'dead spot', or friction, the capsular chamber behind the nozzle does not respond and only 1% of the baffle movement is required to overcome this effect. Thus when a controller sensitivity is reduced pneumatically, as shown in Fig. 35, the performance of the controller at low sensitivity is not handicapped by the increased effect of friction, hysteresis and dead spot in the relay valve. This is a major advantage and most modern controllers utilize this principle.

In the particular design shown in Fig. 35, no provision is made to vary the sensitivity reduction. There are many ways of accomplishing this and one simple system is to move the capsular chamber and nozzle nearer to or farther from the fixed pivot. It is also possible to vary the spring constant of the capsular chamber by a spring adjustment as is shown in Fig. 36.

Information Sheet 6

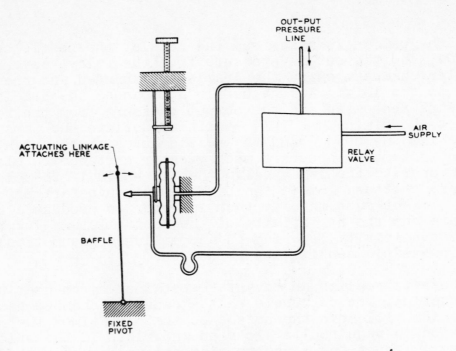

OUT-PUT
PRESSURE
LINE

AIR
SUPPLY

RELAY
VALVE

ACTUATING LINKAGE
ATTACHES HERE

BAFFLE

FIXED
PIVOT

Fig. 36 - Pneumatic Sensitivity Adjustment with
Adjustable Compensation

From the foregoing discussion, it would appear desirable to
design controllers with the highest possible mechanical sensitivity and make provision to reduce this sensitivity through a
wide range pneumatically. This is true, but as has been pointed
out previously, there is a limit at the high sensitivity end of
the range. Furthermore, when the pneumatic sensitivity reduction
becomes great, there is a tendency toward instability in the system. The instrument will 'flutter' or 'pump'. This is undesirable
in most cases and therefore must be avoided. The limit of pneumatic
sensitivity reduction depends upon many factors in the instrument
and is so involved that it is beyond the scope of this text.

Rate Response

When the sensitivity of a controller is reduced pneumatically,
it is possible to provide rate response in the controller by the
addition of a needle valve or restriction in the line to the
sensitivity reducing bellows. See Fig. 37. Let us assume that the
needle valve is partially closed and that the baffle starts to approach the nozzle at a slow rate. The nozzle back pressure begins
to rise and the output pressure from the reverse acting relay valve
starts to fall. This output pressure is connected directly or
indirectly to the diaphragm motor so an immediate response occurs
at the valve. The sensitivity reducing bellows does not immediately
respond to the change in the output pressure due to the presence

Information Sheet 6

of the needle valve and therefore the controller starts to behave like a high sensitivity controller. In other words, the first motion of the baffle causes a big change in the output pressure.

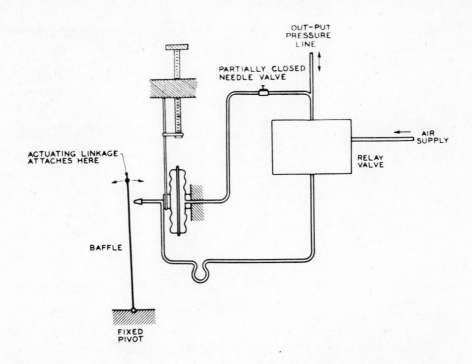

Fig. 37 - Method of Obtaining Rate Response

As the baffle continues to approach the nozzle the output pressure continues to fall and as a pressure differential is created across the needle valve, air flows from the sensitivity reducing bellows and it begins to respond to the decreasing pressure. Eventually, a balance will be reached so that the baffle is approaching the nozzle at substantially the same rate as the nozzle is withdrawing from the baffle. This is pneumatic sensitivity reduction as outlined previously, but note that a pressure differential must be built up across the needle valve before it occurs. Now if the pressure will drop roughly twice as far as before, the nozzle and baffle move at substantially the same rate. Thus it can be seen that this initial response of a controller with this feature is proportional to the rate of change of the primary element which moves the baffle. This response can be increased by increasing the restriction of the needle valve.

Information Sheet 6

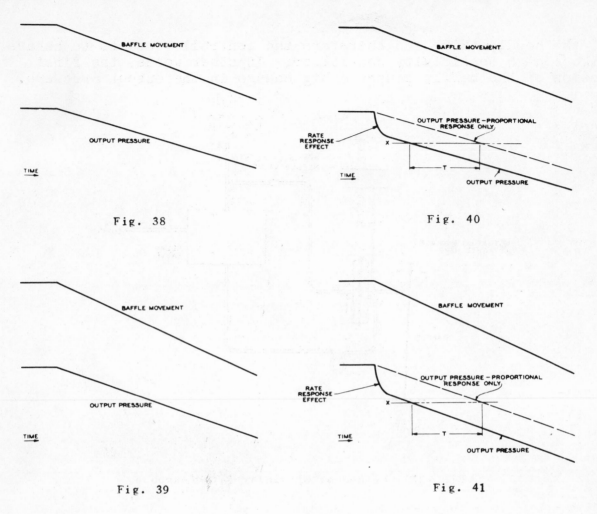

Fig. 38

Fig. 40

Fig. 39

Fig. 41

Fig. 38 gives a comparison of the baffle movement to the output pressure response of a proportional controller. The horizontal portion of the curves represent a period during which there is no change in baffle movement or output pressure. As soon as there is a change in the baffle movement there is a subsequent change in output pressure. The rate of change of output pressure is always proportional to the rate of movement of the baffle.

If the baffle approaches the nozzle at an increased rate, Fig. 39, the output pressure response will still be proportional.

Fig. 40 gives a comparison of the baffle movement and output pressure rates of a controller with rate response. When the rate response needle valve is partially closed, an initial change in the output pressure occurs, which did not previously exist. This is called the rate response effect. Note that the output pressure reaches any given value such as X, T minutes earlier than it would without rate response. T is called the rate time. Now when the rate of motion of the baffle increases, Fig. 41, the rate response effect increases but the rate time, T, remains unchanged.

Information Sheet 6

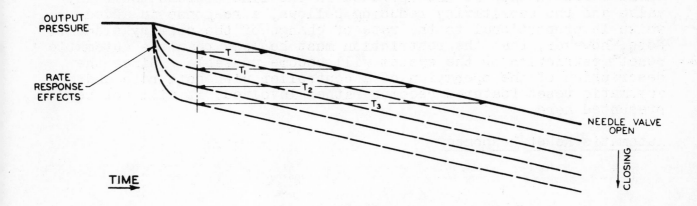

Fig. 42 - Various Output Pressure Responses and
Variations of Rate Time Produced with
Five Successive Needle Valve Settings

Fig. 42 shows the various output pressure responses obtained at five different settings of the needle valve. Note that as the needle valve is positioned from open towards closed that the rate response effect increases and the rate time increases.

Since the rate time is a function only of the opening of the needle valve, the valve is usually calibrated in minutes.

It is worth noting that as soon as the baffle stops moving toward the nozzle, the output pressure will stop falling and as the pressure leaks from the sensitivity reducing bellows, the gap between the baffle and nozzle will widen and the output pressure will rise. When equilibrium is restored with no baffle motion, the output pressure and the pressure in the sensitivity reducing bellows will be identical and will have the same value as if the needle valve had not been incorporated in the circuit. Thus the rate response effect is a transient effect which depends upon the rate of change of the primary element.

While the previous discussion has been based on the assumption that the baffle is approaching the nozzle in Fig. 37 and the relay valve is reverse-acting, it applies equally well to all controllers incorporating pneumatic sensitivity reduction. Of course, if a direct-acting relay valve is used in place of the reverse-acting type, the bellows location must be changed so that the sensitivity is still reduced.

When desired, the rate response may be incorporated into either of the controllers with reset response illustrated schematically in Figs. 43 and 44. If a needle valve or other

Information Sheet 6

similar restriction is incorporated in the line between the relay
valve and the sensitivity reducing bellows, a response is added
which is proportional to the rate of change of the primary element.
Note, however, that the restriction must be less than the automatic
reset restriction or the system will become unstable. Since the
description of the operation of a controller with both rate and
automatic reset features becomes rather involved, it will not be
presented here.

Automatic Reset Response

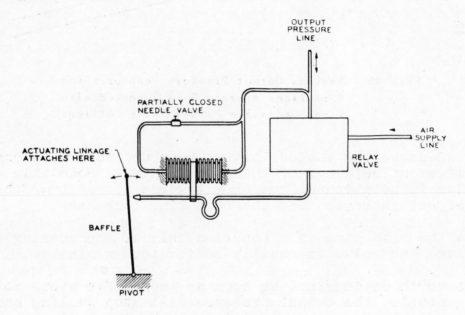

Fig. 43 - Method of Obtaining Automatic Reset Response
with Two Bellows

     In all of the systems discussed so far in this section it
will be noted that there is a definite correspondence between
the measuring element, the Bourdon tube, for example, and the
resulting change in the output pressure from the relay valve.
From Information Sheet 4, it may be seen that as the sensitivity
of the controller is lowered, a new control effect, namely automatic
reset response, becomes more and more important. One of the simple
ways to look at the automatic reset response is to consider it as
a means for gradually restoring the controlled variable to its
original value after a load change. If it were not for this automatic reset response, every load change which means the valve must
move to a different position, would require a change in the value
of the controlled variable in order to obtain this new valve
position. This permanent deviation is objectionable on most control applications, so automatic reset has become more and more
popular even though it adds to the cost of a controller.

Information Sheet 6

There are many ways of incorporating the automatic reset response in a controller, but in most modern instruments they can be grouped into one of two classes. Some automatic reset mechanisms utilize a principle which might be called a cancellation of the sensitivity reduction. Others utilize a feedback of the relay valve output pressure.

Fig. 43 illustrates an automatic reset mechanism in which the sensitivity is first reduced by one bellows, and then a second bellows gradually cancels this sensitivity reduction. It will be noted that this control mechanism is very similar to that illustrated in Fig. 35, with the addition of an extra bellows and needle valve. With this control system it is essential that the mechanical sensitivity of the controller be high, and the sensitivity reduction be accomplished pneumatically. Let us assume that we have a controller of this type in operation and that the baffle is throttling the air discharging from the nozzle so that the nozzle back pressure is 3 psi and the output pressure from the relay valve is 10 psi. The needle valve is partially closed and the pressure in both of the bellows is 10 psi. While auxiliary springs are not shown in the figure, these are generally incorporated in a controller to assist in restoring the bellows to the neutral position as soon as the pressures within the two bellows become equal.

Now, if the Bourdon tube or other measuring element moves the baffle toward the nozzle, the nozzle back pressure will increase and the output pressure from the relay valve will decrease. This lowered relay valve pressure affects the right-hand bellows immediately and it moves the nozzle in the same direction as the baffle. While the left-hand bellows must expand as the right-hand bellows contracts, the volume change in the left-hand system is small, and for our purpose this volume change is negligible. The needle valve in the line leading to the left-hand bellows prevents the change in the output pressure of the relay valve from immediately affecting this bellows through the connecting line. Hence the baffle has to move a much greater distance to close the nozzle under the existing conditions than if the right-hand bellows did not respond to the output pressure of the relay valve. Therefore, this bellows reduces the sensitivity of the controller, and its operation is substantially the same as that shown in Fig. 35. Now, let us assume that the motion of the baffle has been just great enough to cause a 2 psi change in the right-hand bellows, namely from 10 to 8 psi. A 2 psi pressure differential will therefore exist across the needle valve, and air will gradually flow from the left-hand bellows through the needle valve and the relay valve exhaust port to the atmosphere. As this occurs, the left-hand bellows tends to contract and the right to expand, until the pressure becomes equalized in the two bellows. This tends to push the nozzle against the baffle. The nozzle back pressure increases slightly, and as a

Information Sheet 6

result, the relay output pressure diminishes just enough to prevent
an appreciable nozzle motion. Now the only way the nozzle may be
prevented from moving to the left is to maintain a 2 psi differential between the left and right-hand bellows. At the same time,
the pressure on the left-hand bellows is gradually falling, due to
the escape of air through the needle valve. Therefore, the output
pressure of the relay valve, which is also the pressure on the
right-hand bellows, gradually falls until it reaches zero.

Now, if the original motion of the baffle were only half as
great, the initial output pressure change would have been only 1
psi and the pressure drop across the needle valve would have been
only half its previous value. Then the pressure in the left-hand
bellows would have dropped about half as fast, and the same is true
of the relay valve output pressure. Thus, it may be seen that the
immediate change of the output pressure is proportional to the
movement of the baffle, and the subsequent rate of change of the
output pressure is proportional to this same movement. Thus, this
system has produced a proportional and automatic reset response
according to our earlier definition.

The operation which was outlined in the previous paragraph
would be exactly true if the nozzle, baffle and relay valve combination were infinitely sensitive. In other words, this would be
true only if the pressure changes in the bellows could be accomplished without appreciable movement of the baffle relative to the
nozzle. Still another way to state this is that the explanation is
rigorous only if the gap between the baffle and nozzle does not
change as the output pressure and the pressure in the bellows vary
through their total range. While it is possible to design a nozzle, baffle and relay combination which will perform this, it is
not customary to do so. In actual practice the change in the distance between the baffle and the nozzle is so small in comparison
with the movement of the bellows that it can be neglected. It is
beyond the scope of this text to pursue this matter further, but
this variation must be considered in designing controllers.

In actual service, the operation of the mechanism is not
quite as simple as set forth above. The baffle is continually
moving, in response to changes in the apparatus under control, and
the output pressure is continually moving a valve to correct for
these variations. However, by adding together the output pressure
changes resulting from a series of infinitesimal movements of the
baffle, the complete output pressure change may be obtained.
After a load change which changes the position of the baffle, a
differential is set up across the needle valve, and this differential pressure continues to exist until the baffle is restored to
its original position. This means that the corrective action

Information Sheet 6

continues to occur at the control valve until the temperature or
other controlled variable has been restored to its original value.
Hence it is the return of the controlled variable to its original
value which returns the baffle to its original position. Second,
a closer study shows that in reality the baffle has not returned
to its exact original position, but the baffle has changed its relationship to the nozzle just enough to create the required change
in the output pressure from the relay valve. Thus, the original
control point has not been restored completely but the shift is
extremely small, namely, just that required to change the nozzle
back pressure sufficiently to cause the corresponding change in
the output pressure from the relay valve. If the mechanical sensitivity of the controller is high, this small shift in the control
point may be neglected.

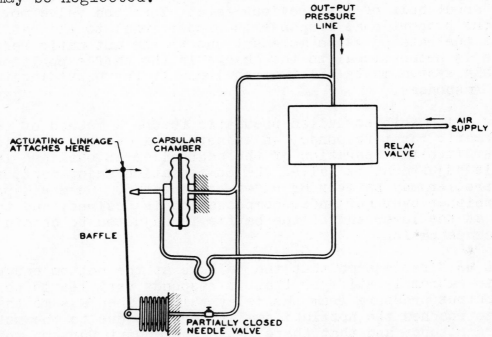

Fig. 44 - Method of Obtaining Automatic Reset Response
Using a Single Bellows

A second method of obtaining the automatic reset response is
illustrated in Fig. 44. This schematic diagram again resembles
Fig. 35 with the exception that a needle valve and bellows have
been added. Again, springs are not shown in this diagram although
they are normally incorporated in a controller. Assuming that the
baffle approaches the nozzle due to the motion of the actuating
element, the nozzle back pressure increases, causing the output pressure from the relay valve to diminish. The capsular chamber behind
the nozzle deflates and moves the nozzle in the same direction as
the baffle. This again is pneumatic sensitivity reduction, and the
operation is identical with that illustrated in Fig. 35. Note that

Information Sheet 6

due to the motion of the nozzle, it takes quite an appreciable baffle motion to change the output pressure from the relay valve. Now, as this output pressure from the relay valve diminishes, a differential pressure is set up across the needle valve, and pressure gradually bleeds from the bellows mounted at the lower end of the baffle. As this bellows contracts, the nozzle is closed an additional amount, and the output pressure from the relay valve continues to diminish. This will continue due to the operation of the bellows at the lower end of the baffle alone, without further motion from the measuring element, until the output pressure from the relay valve reaches zero. If the initial motion of the primary element or the baffle is only half that which was assumed before, the initial output pressure change from the relay valve will be cut in half, approximately, and the rate of pressure fall towards zero will be about half of its previous rate. Thus the valve movement due to the proportional response is proportional to the baffle motion and the rate of valve movement due to the automatic reset response is proportional to the change in the baffle position. Thus, this system meets all the requirements for providing these two control responses.

Now, with this so-called pneumatic feedback method of obtaining automatic reset response, an adjustment is necessary which did not enter into the operation of the controller as outlined in Fig. 43. This adjustment is called the compensation adjustment, since the controller may be over or under-compensated. On most applications, neither over nor under-compensation is desired, and the bellows at the lower end of the baffle is adjusted to obtain 'complete' compensation.

Let us first assume that the bellows at the bottom end of the baffle is extremely stiff so that it responds very little to changes in the output pressure from the relay valve. Then assume that the baffle approaches the nozzle a small increment due to the motion of the Bourdon tube, and that there is no subsequent further motion of the Bourdon tube. There will be an initial output pressure change due to the proportional response, and a subsequent gradual change due to the automatic reset response, but this will gradually die out because the stiff bellows does not feed enough motion back to perpetuate the automatic reset response. The effect on the output pressure might be something like that shown in Fig. 45c. With this set-up it may be seen that the rate of change of output pressure is not proportional to the original deviation, for the rate should eventually diminish to zero. Therefore, this does not meet all our requirements for an automatic reset response.

If, on the other hand, we assume that the bellows at the bottom of the baffle lever is extremely flexible so that a great deal of motion is fed back at this point, then the rate of change of

Information Sheet 6

output pressure will not remain constant, but will increase as illustrated in Fig. 45b. Again, this does not meet our requirements
for an automatic reset response. Now between these two values for
the stiffness of this bellows, there is one correct value which
provides a constant rate of output pressure change as illustrated
in Fig. 45a. This meets our requirements for an automatic reset
response and is substantially identical with that obtained from the
controller illustrated in Fig. 43.

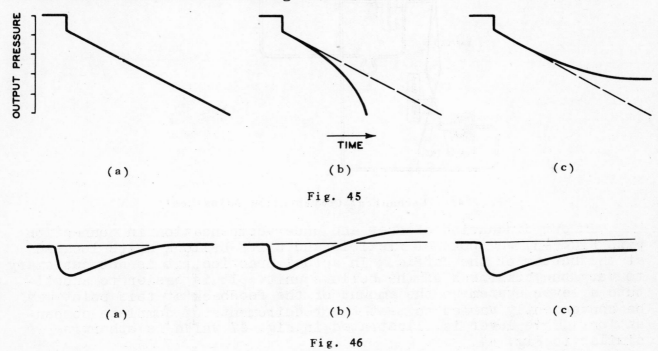

Fig. 45

Fig. 46

    With the controller in this adjustment, the controlled variable
will return to the original control point after a load change, as
illustrated in Fig. 46a, while the performance illustrated in Fig.
46c corresponds to the output pressure change shown in Fig. 45c and
46b corresponds with 45b. Note that in Fig. 46c the controlled
variable does not return all the way to the control point, and this
is called 'under-compensation'. In Fig. 46b the controlled variable
crosses over the control point, and this is called 'over-compensa-
tion'. Complete compensation is illustrated in Fig. 46a and is
obtained from a perfect automatic reset response.

    Before leaving Fig. 44, it should be pointed out that this
delayed feedback system of obtaining automatic reset response would
be effective, if used with mechanical sensitivity reduction. In
other words, it is immaterial whether the original low sensitivity
is obtained mechanically, as illustrated in Fig. 34, or whether it
is done pneumatically, as illustrated in Fig. 35. Of course, the
pneumatic method of sensitivity reduction still has the advantages
which were set forth in our discussion of Fig. 35.

Information Sheet 6

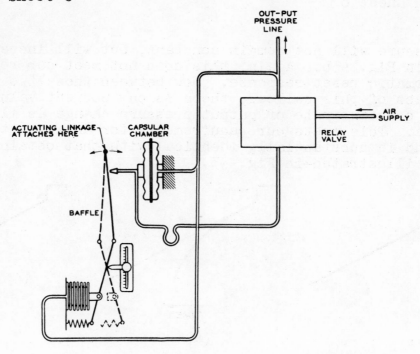

Fig. 47 - Mechanical Compensation Adjustment

In our discussion of over and under-compensation in connection with Fig. 45, we spoke of flexible and stiff bellows units located at the bottom of the baffle. In actual practice, it is not customary to vary the stiffness of the bellows unit. It is easier to substitute a lever system so the amount of the feedback at this point may be conveniently varied to meet the requirements of complete compensation. This lever is illustrated in Fig. 47 which is otherwise similar to Fig. 44.

Another design element which is of particular importance in controllers which must indicate or record, as well as control, is the over-throw mechanism. In instruments of this class it is essential that the indication or record be practically independent from the control mechanism. This means that the baffle must not impede the movement of the measuring element as it strikes the nozzle. Over-throw mechanisms prevent the nozzle from interfering with the motion of the measuring element.

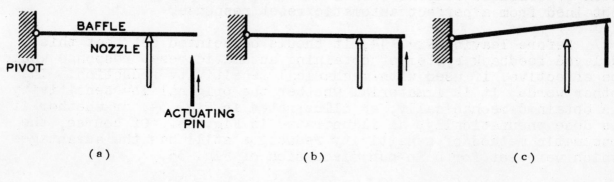

Fig. 48

Information Sheet 6

One type of over-throw mechanism is illustrated in Fig. 48. The baffle is held against the nozzle by the force of gravity acting on the mass of the baffle. The measuring element actuates the pin which approaches the baffle, Fig. 48b, and lifts the baffle from the nozzle, Fig. 48c. Note that the only hindrance to the motion of the measuring element is the added weight of the baffle as it is lifted from the nozzle.

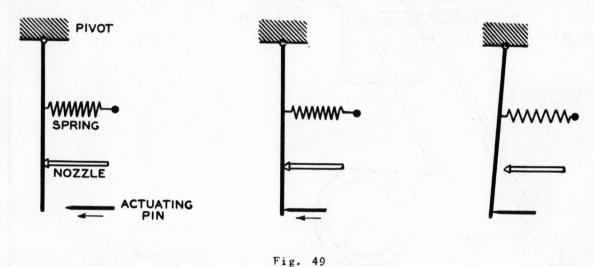

Fig. 49

Almost the same thing can be accomplished by means of a spring as illustrated in Fig. 49. With this system, the force on the primary element is slightly increased as the baffle is moved farther and farther away from the nozzle. This is undesirable but it will not be objectionable if the spring constant is made sufficiently small. Note that with the first over-throw system the weight of the baffle must be sufficiently great to back up sufficient pressure in the nozzle, and with the second system the initial tension in the spring must accomplish the same thing. Thus the force required from the Bourdon tube or other measuring element is less when the nozzle is small and when the gain in the relay valve is great. Another way to state this same thing is that the error introduced in the indication or record is less when the nozzle is small and the relay valve gain is high. This error, though small, is often observable and is called the instrument detent.

Information Sheet 7   PNEUMATIC MECHANISMS INCORPORATING CONTROL

EFFECTS

The Taylor Fulscope Controller

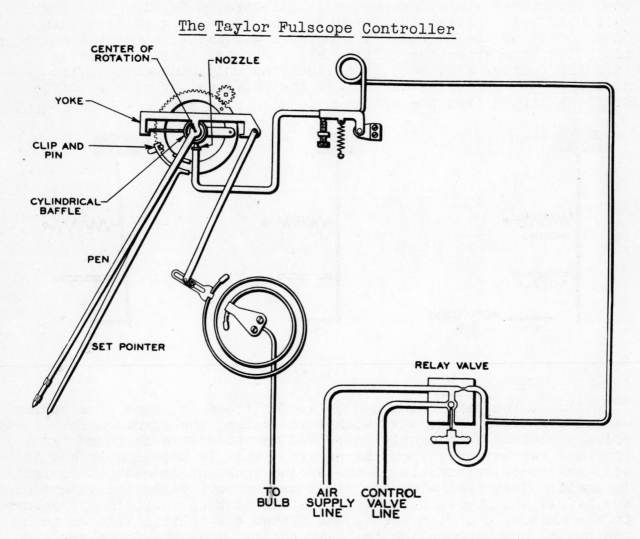

Fig. 50 - Schematic Diagram of Taylor Controller - Fixed High Sensitivity Type
Courtesy of Taylor Instrument Companies

Fig. 50 is a schematic diagram of the Taylor Controller of the high sensitivity type. In this instrument, the sensitivity is fixed at a value in the neighborhood of 1000 psi per inch, and therefore is limited to those applications which are easy to control. Generally, this means that they must have a short time lag and a relatively large capacity.

The unique feature of this instrument is the

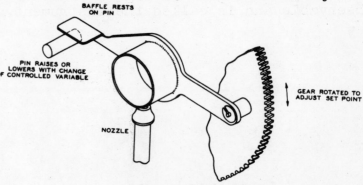

Fig. 51 - The Cylindrical Baffle

Information Sheet 7

cylindrical baffle, Fig. 51, which permits a construction with a very few pivots and facilitates reversal of the instrument. Generally speaking, a direct-acting, air-operated controller is one in which the output air pressure increases as the pen or pointer moves upward on the scale or chart. A reverse-acting instrument is one whose output pressure diminishes as the pen or pointer moves upward on the scale or chart. These general rules result in some confusion in a few cases, but the exceptions are few and need no further explanation at this time.

Referring again to Fig. 50, let us assume that the temperature as indicated by the pen is higher than that desired as recorded by the set pointer, so that the yoke has lifted the cylindrical baffle away from the nozzle. Since the nozzle is larger than the orifice, the pressure in the nozzle line and in the capsular chamber is low. The ball in the relay valve is against the lower seat, and the full air supply pressure is applied to the diaphragm valve, closing the valve supplying heat to the process. As the temperature falls, the pen approaches the set pointer, and the baffle approaches the nozzle. If the instrument is properly adjusted, when the pen passes the set pointer, the baffle closes the nozzle, building up pressure in the nozzle line and in the capsular chamber, which in turn forces the ball against the upper seat of the relay valve. Pressure bleeds from the diaphragm motor opening the steam valve, which again supplies heat to the process. The reverse effect occurs as the temperature rises, and therefore, it will be seen that if the time lag on the application is short, the pen will be maintained very close to the set pointer.

In this particular controller, it requires about .001" movement of the pen to produce an output pressure change on the diaphragm valve of one pound per square inch. Therefore, in order to produce the full 20 pounds per square inch output pressure change, which is the normal air supply specified for this instrument, .020" pen motion is required. This distance is so small in relation to the distance between consecutive divisions on the chart that this controller is often called an on and off instrument.

This instrument has the 'direct set' feature. When it is in proper adjustment, the set pointer may be adjusted to any desired temperature by means of the small gear, and the opening and closing of the nozzle will occur only when the pen passes the set pointer. In other words, the set point may be fixed at any desired temperature on the chart. In this particular instrument, this is accomplished by the rotation of the pivot point on the cylindrical baffle around the center of rotation. The pivot point rotates through the same number of angular degrees as the set pointer. Since the yoke pivots about the same point, the pen must rotate through the same number of angular degrees before it can actuate the nozzle and the relay valve again. Thus in normal operation, the pen must follow the set pointer.

Information Sheet 7

     In order for this instrument to operate properly, the cylin-
drical portion of the baffle must be concentric with the center of
rotation when the pen and the set pointer are together. Adjustments
are provided in the instrument to meet this requirement. Note that
regardless of the position of the pen and set pointer, the baffle
is always tangent to the nozzle so that good closure is insured.·

     This instrument may be changed from direct-acting to reverse-
acting by disengaging the clip from the pin and rotating the baffle
pivot point through 180 angular degrees. The free end of the baffle then rests on the extension on the right side of the yoke.
When adjusted in this way, the baffle closes the nozzle, as the
temperature in the process rises, and the instrument is reverse-
acting.

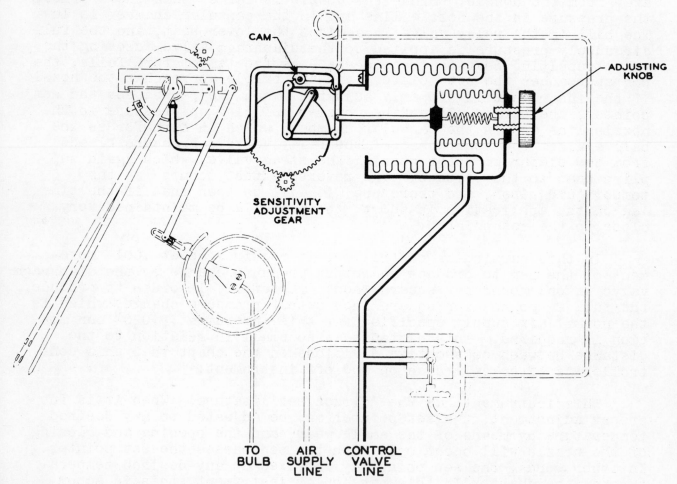

Fig. 52 - Schematic Diagram of Taylor Controller - Adjustable Sensitivity Type
Courtesy of Taylor Instrument Companies

     Fig. 52 illustrates the Taylor Controller of the adjustable
sensitivity type. In this particular instrument, as the baffle
tends to open the nozzle, the output pressure from the relay valve
operates on the outside of the outer bellows to cause the nozzle

Information Sheet 7

to move away from the baffle. This is pneumatic sensitivity reduction as discussed in Information Sheet 6. One feature of this particular instrument is the parallelogram which permits the adjustment of the instrument sensitivity to meet the requirements of the application.

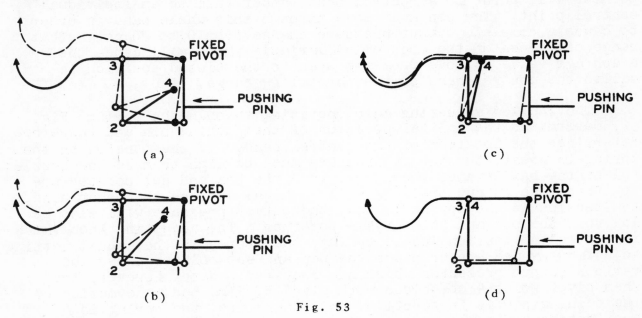

Fig. 53

The operation of the parallelogram may be more easily explained by referring to the simplified diagrams in Fig. 53. Referring first to Fig. 53a, it will be seen that a small amount of motion fed into the parallelogram through the pushing pin causes a small movement of pivot point 1 about the fixed pivot. This in turn results in a rather large motion of pivot point 2 about pivot point 4, and a large motion of pivot point 3 about the fixed pivot. The motion of the nozzle is great, the sensitivity reduction is great, and the instrument sensitivity is low. In Fig. 53b pivot point 4 is moved upward, and the motion of the nozzle resulting from the same motion of the pushing pin is considerably less. The instrument sensitivity is higher. The adjustment illustrated in Fig. 53c results in very little motion of the nozzle for a given motion of the pushing pin, and finally, it will be seen that when pivot point 4 corresponds with pivot point 3, motions of the pushing pin are not transmitted to the nozzle. In this latter adjustment, there is no sensitivity reduction, and the instrument sensitivity, therefore, is high. Apparently, then, the sensitivity of the controller may be conveniently varied by altering the position of pivot point 4. In the Taylor Fulscope Controller, pivot point 4 is moved in an arc about pivot point 2 by means of a knurled knob adjustment. The sensitivity can be varied from 1,000 psi per inch to 1 psi per inch without disturbing the control point, provided the parallelogram is squared. This is one of the standard instrument adjustments, and when the parallelogram is squared, pivot point 2 corresponds with the center of rotation of pivot 4.

Information Sheet 7

Referring again to Fig. 52, it will be seen that in order to completely open and close the nozzle, the pen must travel across a considerable portion of the chart, provided the parallelogram is adjusted so that the nozzle follows the baffle. Therefore, the set pointer will point to a control band rather than to an individual control point. The pen must move through this whole band in order to cause a complete output pressure change from 0 to 20 psi. That range of values of the controlled variable which will cause the diaphragm valve to move from the open to the closed position is called the control band or the throttling range.

The knurled adjusting knob operating through the spring, Fig. 52, determines the initial position of the pushing pin and therefore determines the location of the control band. If the tension on the spring is great, the output pressure must be high to make the nozzle follow the baffle and, therefore, when the pen and set pointer are together, the output pressure will be high. If, on the other hand, the tension in the spring is low, the output pressure will also be low when the pen and pointer are together. The adjusting knob which regulates the tension in the spring, therefore, is the manual setting adjustment which synchronizes the pen and set pointer under the various output pressures which are required. Note, however, that when pivot point 4 coincides with pivot 3, Fig. 53d, the motion of the pushing pin is ineffective, and, therefore, the spring is ineffective. For this reason a cam is provided for synchronization in the high sensitivity position.

The small inner bellows is simply a seal so that the adjustment of the spring may be accomplished without a stuffing box.

Fig. 54 illustrates the Taylor Fulscope Controller with Pre-Act (rate response). Note that the only difference between this controller and the one illustrated in Fig. 52 is the addition of a restriction in the line leading to the large bellows. Since the bellows reduces the sensitivity, the needle valve delays the sensitivity reduction.

Possibly the best way to explain the operation of this controller is to assume that following a period of equilibrium, the temperature in the process starts to rise. As this occurs, the baffle starts to leave the nozzle, and, through the action of the relay valve the output pressure from the controller increases to the diaphragm motor. A differential pressure is created across the orifice in the needle valve, so that the outer bellows and the nozzle do not respond to the output pressure with the same alacrity as they did in the case of the controller illustrated in Fig. 52. As the temperature continues to rise, eventually the pressure differential created across the restriction in the needle valve will be sufficiently great so that the nozzle again moves at the same rate as the baffle. However, the gap between the baffle and nozzle is larger than it would otherwise have been, and, therefore, the output pressure is greater than it otherwise would have been. From a study of the figure, it will be

Information Sheet 7

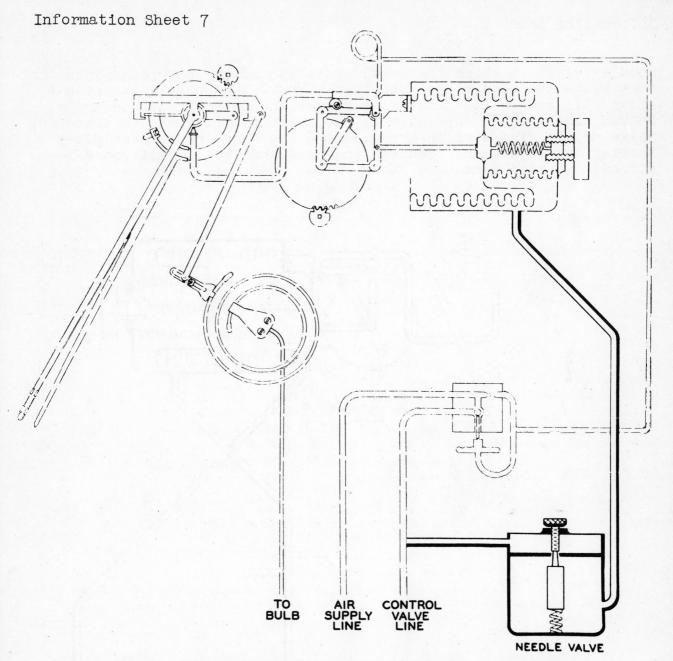

TO
BULB

AIR
SUPPLY
LINE

CONTROL
VALVE
LINE

NEEDLE VALVE

Fig. 54 - Schematic Diagram of Taylor Fulscope Controller with Pre-Act

Courtesy of Taylor Instrument Companies

apparent that if the temperature rises fast, the gap between the baffle and the nozzle will be relatively great, while if the temperature
rises slowly, this gap will be relatively small. Thus the control
effect which results is proportional to the rate of change of the
temperature in the process. The pre-act effect can be adjusted to
meet the requirements of the application by varying the opening of
the needle valve. The needle valve used in this controller has three
features which are worthy of some comment. First, the valve is
reverse-acting (spring closed, manually opened). The needle slides
in and out of an orifice, following the adjustment of the knurled
screw. Since the needle does not turn and cannot be forced into
place by a careless operator, the surface of the needle and of the
seat remain in good condition. This is not true of direct-acting

Information Sheet 7

needle valves in which the needle rotates and may be ground into the seat by a single careless operation. Thus, this particular needle valve will retain its original surfaces and maintain its accuracy. Second, while it is not shown in the schematic diagram, this needle valve may be disassembled for cleaning and checking without disturbing its adjustment. Third, the needle valve is calibrated directly in rate time.

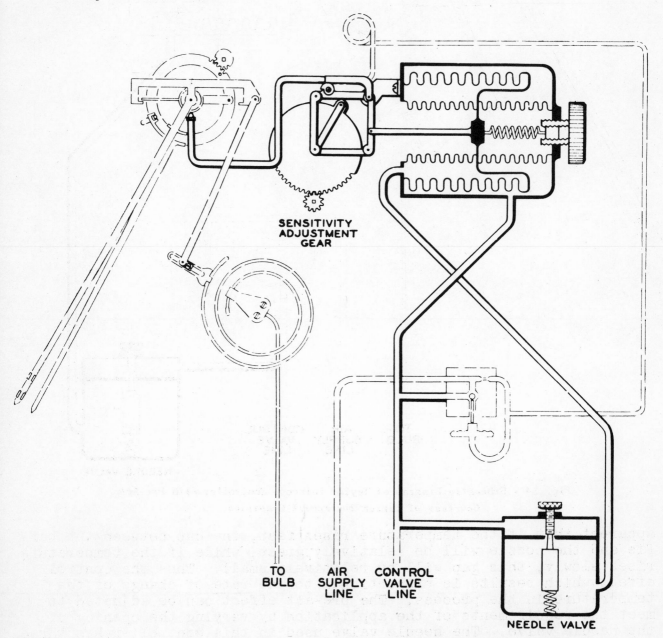

SENSITIVITY
ADJUSTMENT
GEAR

TO
BULB

AIR
SUPPLY
LINE

CONTROL
VALVE
LINE

NEEDLE VALVE

Fig. 55 - Schematic Diagram of Taylor Fulscope Controller with Feset
Courtesy of Taylor Instrument Companies

Fig. 55 illustrates a Taylor Fulscope Controller with Automatic Reset. It will be noted that the needle valve is identical with that used in connection with the pre-act controller of Fig. 54, but

Information Sheet 7

that this time it connects the output pressure from the controller
to the opposite side of the large outer bellows.

In order to explain the operation of this controller, let us assume that the process has been in equilibrium for some time with the
pen and set pointer together and the output pressure at any selected
value, say 9 psi. The pressure on both sides of the large bellows is
9 psi. If the temperature in the process decreases due to a load
change, the pen lowers and the output pressure increases. A pressure
differential occurs across the restriction in the needle valve of the
large bellows. Let us assume that this differential is 2 psi so that
the output pressure differential is just great enough to make the
nozzle move upward to follow the motion of the baffle which has been
moved by the Bourdon tube. Due to the pressure differential, air
flows across the needle valve restriction, tending to build up the
pressure on the inside of the large bellows. This tends to restore
the nozzle towards its original position, but this is prevented by
the nozzle acting through the relay valve to increase the pressure
on the outside of the large bellows. For example, as the pressure
inside the large bellows increases to 9-1/2 psi, the pressure outside
the bellows increases substantially the same amount, and this will
continue as long as the pen is below the set pointer, and the baffle
is below its normal position. Thus, the output pressure of the controller will increase from 11 psi to some higher value, but at the
same time, the pressure inside the bellows will increase at the same
rate so that the 2 psi differential still exists. Eventually, the
resultant motion of the diaphragm valve will result in a temperature
increase, and the pen will approach the set pointer. As this occurs,
a smaller pressure differential will be required across the bellows
to maintain the nozzle in operating relationship with the baffle,
and, therefore, the differential will decrease and the flow across
the orifice of the needle valve will decrease correspondingly.
Eventually, when the pen coincides with the set pointer, the baffle
will be in its original position and the differential pressure across
the bellows will be zero since no differential is required to make
the nozzle follow the baffle. Thus the system is again in equilibrium with the pen and set pointer together with a different pressure
on the diaphragm motor. Note that if the pen deviates a long distance away from the set pointer, the differential pressure across
the bellows will be relatively great, and the rate of output pressure
change will be great. On the other hand, when the deviation of the
pen from the set pointer is small, the differential across the
needle valve orifice is small, and the rate of change of output pressure is roughly proportional to the magnitude of the initial deviation.

Note that this meets the requirements for an automatic reset
response as set forth earlier in this text.

The left inner bellows permits the motion to be taken from the
large bellows by means of the pushing pin without a stuffing box.
The right inner bellows permits the adjustment of the spring by means
of the knurled knob without a stuffing box. Since these two bellows
are of the same diameter, they do not otherwise enter into the

Information Sheet 7

operation of the controller. The sensitivity adjustment in this instrument, like that in the controllers illustrated in Figs. 52 and 54, is accomplished by means of the gear which is turned by a knurled knob.

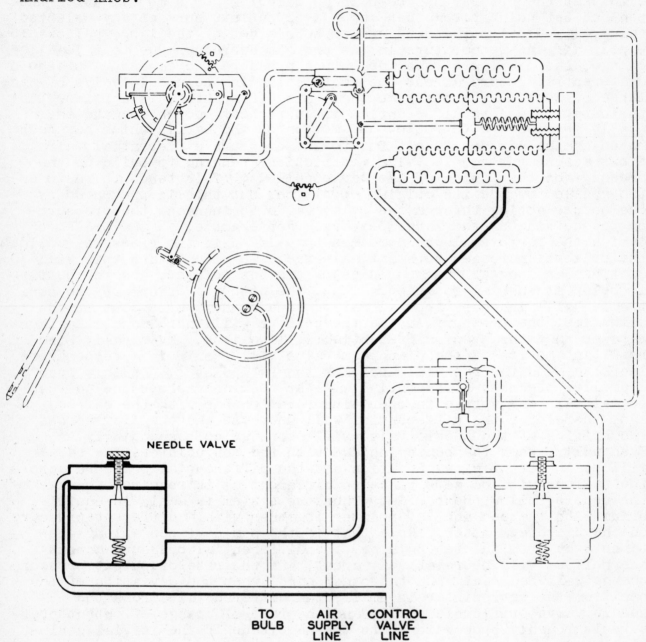

NEEDLE VALVE

TO
BULB

AIR
SUPPLY
LINE

CONTROL
VALVE
LINE

Fig. 56 - Schematic Diagram of Taylor Fulscope Controller with Pre-Act and Reset
Courtesy of Taylor Instrument Companies

Fig. 56 illustrates the Taylor Fulscope Controller with both Pre-Act and Automatic Reset. Since the operation of a controller with three control responses is extremely difficult to explain without resorting to mathematics, this instrument will not be

Information Sheet 7

covered in detail. It is worth noting, however, that if the right needle valve restriction and the left needle valve restriction retard the pressure changes on both sides of the large bellows the same amount, the bellows does not respond, and the instrument behaves as a high sensitivity controller, as illustrated in Fig. 50. Therefore, to obtain the control responses, the left needle must be opened more than the right needle valve. As these particular needle valves are calibrated directly in pre-act time and reset rate, another way to make this same statement is to say that the product of the pre-act time and the reset rate must be less than 1. Actually, on many applications, the best performance is obtained when this product is in the neighborhood of 1/3.

Fig. 57 - Cut-away View of Taylor Fulscope Controller with Pre-Act and Reset
Courtesy of Taylor Instrument Companies

Fig. 57 is a cut-away view of the Taylor Fulscope Controller with Automatic Reset and Pre-Act. The knob which adjusts the direct set pointer is shown at the top center of the case. The sensitivity adjustment is to the right and slightly below it. The pre-act

Information Sheet 7

needle valve and automatic reset needle valve are at the lower left-hand and right-hand center of the case respectively. The relay valve is at the right center of the case, and the clock which drives the chart is just below the center of the case. This instrument, like most instruments of this class, is available in the 'double-duty' form. 'Double-duty' instruments are particularly valuable when two related variables are to be controlled together, for example, the wet and dry bulb temperatures on an air conditioning application. In this particular instrument, corresponding left-hand mechanisms are available so that a second complete recording and controlling unit may be installed in this same case. If both pre-act and automatic reset are required on the 'double-duty' instrument, it is customary to locate the pre-act needle valves external to the case proper.

Fig. 58 - Taylor Fulscope Controller with Pre-Act and Reset
Courtesy of Taylor Instrument Companies

The knobs for adjusting the control effects on the 'single-duty' instrument are better shown in Fig. 58.

Information Sheet 7

The Foxboro Stabilog Controller

The Foxboro Model 30 Stabilog Controller is a general purpose instrument. It features various interchangeable unit assemblies which are used to provide a range of control effects.

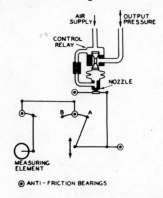

Fig. 59 - Schematic Diagram of
Foxboro On-Off Controller

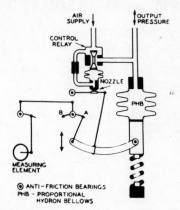

Fig. 60 - Schematic Diagram of
Foxboro Proportional Controller

Courtesy of Foxboro Company

Fig. 59 is a schematic diagram of the Foxboro On-Off Controller. A measuring element actuates the control relay by means of a lever system. The nozzle is actually mounted as a part of the relay setting yoke assembly and the flapper is driven by the reversing link. As the flapper approaches the nozzle it inflates the relay bellows which raises the relay pilot and opens the air supply, increasing the output pressure of the controller. When the flapper moves away from the nozzle the relay pilot is lowered to cut off the air supply and bleed air from the output line.

The proportional controller, Fig. 60, utilizes a lever system known as the proportioning arc lever system. Proportional band adjustment is accomplished by moving the link beneath the flapper to various positions along the proportioning arc lever.

The proportioning hydron bellows and spring combination shown at the right of the figure tend to increase the proportional band as follows: As the flapper moves away from the nozzle to decrease the controller output pressure the proportioning bellows deflates and is pushed upward by the spring. This action tends to move the flapper towards the nozzle reducing its effective movement and thereby increasing the proportional band.

The following explanation of the Stabilog Reset Controller is based on the operation of the proportioning arc-lever as effected through the control relay. The arc-lever rotates about the proportioning fulcrum, which for all practical purposes is a fixed

Information Sheet 7

pivot point. One end is operated by the bellows and the other end by the measuring element through the bellcrank. The deflection of the bellcrank and hence of the arc-lever is proportional to the deviation of the pen from the setting index, due to the mechanics of the system. As a result, the movement of the proportioning bellows is proportional to the deviation of the measurement from the control point. The control relay plays the major part in effecting this action.

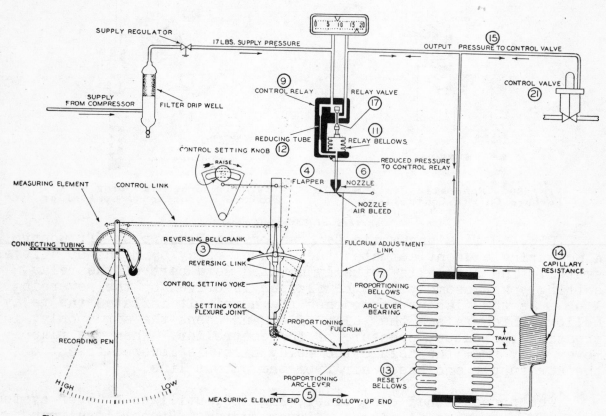

Fig. 61 - Schematic Diagram of Foxboro Stabilog Controller with Reset Response
Courtesy of Foxboro Company

The control relay bleeds air to or from the proportioning bellows in exactly the right amounts to maintain the proper air pressure in the output line and in the proportioning bellows. This enables arc-lever 5, Fig. 61, to rotate about the proportioning fulcrum as a fixed pivot.

The balanced position of the flapper-nozzle occurs with the flapper almost touching the nozzle and a small amount of air escaping. If the flapper approaches the nozzle, pressure builds up in the relay bellows and the relay passes more air to the proportioning bellows. This lowers the proportioning arc-lever and tends to move the flapper away from the nozzle again. If the flapper departs from the nozzle, air is bled from the proportioning bellows. This lifts the proportioning arc-lever and tends to restore the flapper to its original position. The system is therefore self-balancing.

Information Sheet 7

In the action described above, the motion of the flapper is infinitesimal so that the lower end of the fulcrum adjustment link is practically a fixed point. Consequently, the proportioning arc-lever pivots about the proportioning fulcrum, and the motion of the bellows is proportional to the deflection of the pen.

Under balanced conditions, the pen is at the setting index, the reversing bellcrank is in its balanced position, and the same pressure exists in the proportioning and reset bellows. If an upset occurs making the element read lower, the reversing bellcrank will move, raising the measuring element end of proportioning arc-lever 5. Due to the action described in the previous section, air is immediately fed to the proportioning bellows to lower it an equivalent amount. As bellows 7 is spring-loaded, a greater air pressure is necessary to obtain this expanded position, thus creating a uniform proportional band in which the output air pressure change is made proportional to the element deflection.

With reset response, assume that an upset has occurred and the proportioning action described in the last section has taken place. The increased pressure in bellows 7 immediately starts to bleed through capillary resistance 14 to reset bellows 13, which is equal in area to and opposes the motion of bellows 7. However, the proportioning bellows must remain in the expanded position as long as the element remains deflected, due to the arc-lever rotating rigidly about a fixed pivot. The result is that the pressures in both the proportioning and reset bellows will rise, with a fixed differential pressure between them, until such time as the control valve is sufficiently opened, and the process reacts to move the pen and the bellcrank back to their balanced positions. As this occurs, the pressures in the proportioning and reset bellows balance, and they assume their original balanced position. A different pressure, however, may now exist in the motor, the proportioning bellows, and the reset bellows than existed before the upset.

As has been developed previously, the deflection of outer bellows 7, Fig. 62, must be proportional to the deflection of the pen. Hence, when the pen is moving due to an upset, the bellows moves at a rate proportional to the rate at which the pen is deviating.

In derivative or rate response controllers, a capillary restriction called derivative resistance, 16, is inserted between the control relay and outer bellows 7. If an upset occurs, causing the pen to deviate and this bellows to expand at a fixed rate, air flows into the bellows at a fixed rate. This creates a fixed pressure drop across the derivative resistance. If, however, the rate of pen deviation changes and the bellows expands more rapidly, air must flow more rapidly into the bellows creating a greater pressure drop across the derivative resistance. Hence, the pressure drop across the derivative resistance, defined as the derivative effect,

Information Sheet 7

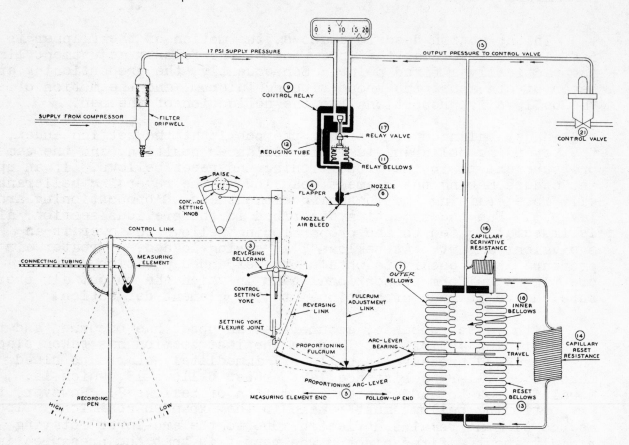

Fig. 62 - Schematic Diagram of Foxboro Stabilog Hyper-Reset Controller

Courtesy of Foxboro Company

is proportional to the rate of pen deviation. As a result, the pressure in the output line is higher than that in the outer bellows by the pressure drop across the derivative resistance, or by an amount proportional to the rate of pen deviation.

In the Hyper-Reset Derivative Controller, inner bellows 18 is provided for reasons of stability. It is connected directly to the controller output and serves to modify the derivative action, reducing the objectionable effects of mechanical vibration and jarring.

The above explanation of control action starts with the controller in successful control of the process. Of course, the controller must have been adjusted to the process. Assuming the proper control valve selection so that failure of supply air pressure will cause the valve to go open or shut as is safer for the process, the desired control action is selected by shifting the reversing link, which is shown in Fig. 62.

Adjustment of proportioning band is made by moving the proportioning fulcrum along the proportioning arc-lever. With the fulcrum toward the right, a relatively large measurement motion is balanced

Information Sheet 7

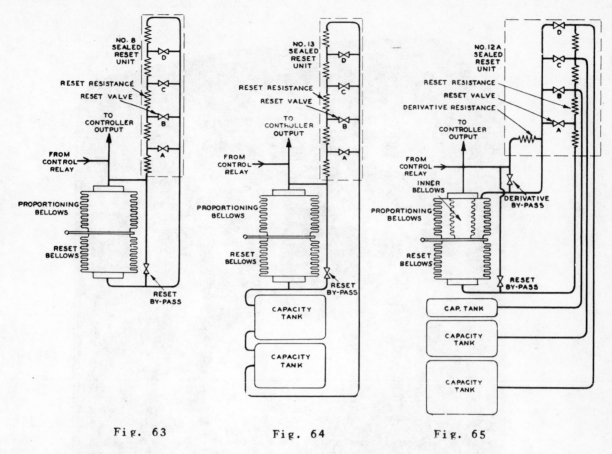

Fig. 63   Fig. 64   Fig. 65

Courtesy of Foxboro Company

by a small bellows motion, air pressure change and valve action; hence a wide proportioning band results for unresponsive processes. Toward the right, the proportioning band is narrow.

Adjustment of the reset time of reset controllers to a time safely longer than the process recovery time is accomplished by opening one of the reset resistance valves, Fig. 63. These are by-pass valves which adjust the effective capillary resistance length in large steps. Capacity tanks, Fig. 64, add volume and multiply the reset times several-fold on units for processes requiring long reset times. On the Hyper-Reset unit, the circuit network is so arranged that opening any reset valve sets both the reset and the derivative times to properly related values. This can best be followed by tracing the diagram four times and distinctively coloring the derivative outer bellows and reset bellows air paths, one diagram for each reset valve open. See Fig. 65. Only one valve is opened at a time per instructions on the instrument chart plate. For some readers the action will be clearer by noting the analogy to radio filter circuits. Reset times range from a fraction of a minute with A open on a pressure-flow unit, to several hours of time on an averaging liquid level unit. A Hyper-Reset temperature unit with no valve open gives proportional derivative action.

Information Sheet 7

Fig. 66 - Internal View of Foxboro Stabilog Hyper-Reset Controller

Courtesy of Foxboro Company

Fig. 66 shows the Foxboro Hyper-Reset Controller. The reducing valve is in the upper-left-hand corner of the case. The air supply and air output gages are combined in a single unit located at the top center. The measuring element is at the left center. The control point adjustment is in the center of the case just below the air gages, and below this is the actuating lever system. The proportioning arc-lever is above and to the right of the clock. Its right end extends into a metal container which houses the double bellows assembly. The relay valve and the manual to

Information Sheet 7

automatic switch are just to the right of the air gages, and the
four screws for adjusting the reset rate are in the upper right-
hand corner of the case.

Fig. 67 - Foxboro Stabilog Controller with Hyper-Reset
Courtesy of Foxboro Company

Fig. 67 is an illustration of this same instrument with the
chart and plate in place. Note the four reset rate adjustment
screws and the knurled knob adjustment directly below, which sets
the proportional band.

Information Sheet 7

The Brown Air-O-Line Controller

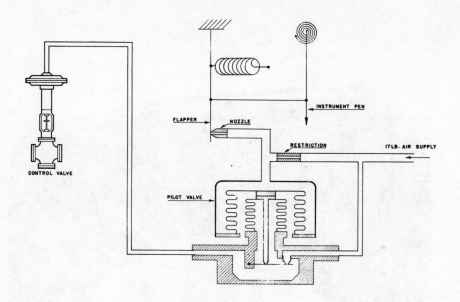

Fig. 68 - Schematic Diagram of Brown Air-O-Line
On-Off Controller
Courtesy of Brown Instrument Company

The Brown On-and-Off Controller has many features in common
with the Taylor and Foxboro instruments of this same class which
were covered in detail previously. Referring to Fig. 68, it will
be seen that the Bourdon tube operates a baffle or flapper which
opens and closes a nozzle. As is the case with the previous instruments, this instrument may be actuated by a temperature sensitive element, a pressure measuring device, or any other measuring
element. The nozzle is supplied with air through a restriction,
and the nozzle back pressure actuates a pilot valve. In this
particular instrument, the pilot valve is of the non-bleed type
which has been described previously.

Fig. 69 is a schematic diagram of the Brown Throttlor Controller which provides a limited sensitivity adjustment. The throttling
range of this instrument is from 1 to 10%. The throttling range
or sensitivity adjustment is accomplished mechanically by manually
changing the length of the levers between the Bourdon tube and the
baffle. This instrument, like all Brown Controllers of this class,
has a manual reset adjustment not shown in the figure, which
adjusts the valve output pressure. In other words, the pen may be
brought back to the control pointer by this adjustment when a load
change occurs.

The Brown Full Throttlor Controller is similar in construction

Information Sheet 7

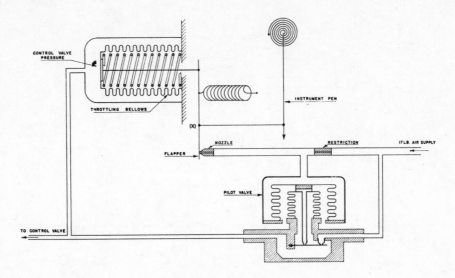

CONTROL VALVE
PRESSURE

THROTTLING BELLOWS

INSTRUMENT PEN

(X)

FLAPPER

NOZZLE

RESTRICTION

17 LB. AIR SUPPLY

PILOT VALVE

TO CONTROL VALVE

Fig. 69 - Schematic Diagram of Brown Air-O-Line
Throttlor Controller
Courtesy of Brown Instrument Company

to the Throttlor Controller but has a wider operating range. It
will be noted that in both the Throttlor and the Full Throttlor
controllers a bellows and spring have been added to the on-and-off
controller in such a manner that the output pressure from the
relay valve reduces the instrument's sensitivity. The method of
adjusting the sensitivity of the Full Throttlor Controller is accomplished by varying the length of the levers which connect the
bellows to the baffle or flapper. The throttling range may be
adjusted to from 1 to 150% of the chart range. As is the case
with the Throttlor Controller, a manual reset adjustment is provided
to return the pen to the pointer after each load change.

The Brown Instrument which incorporates automatic reset is
illustrated in Fig. 70. This instrument is somewhat different
from the corresponding instruments manufactured by other companies
in that it utilizes liquid damping in obtaining the automatic reset
response. The best way to explain the operation of this instrument
is to assume that the baffle moves away from the nozzle operating
the relay valve and reducing the instrument output pressure. The
movable ends of all four bellows will move to the left, since the
compression in the helical spring at the right is greater than the
force due to the reduced pressure on the left-hand bellows. Since
this action is very quick, practically no fluid flows through the
needle valve, and the motion to the left continues until the
springs inside the hydrons offset the unbalance from the low output
pressure and the helical spring at the right. Note that this
motion is applied to the upper end of the baffle or flapper so that
the instrument sensitivity is reduced. In this operation, the

Information Sheet 7

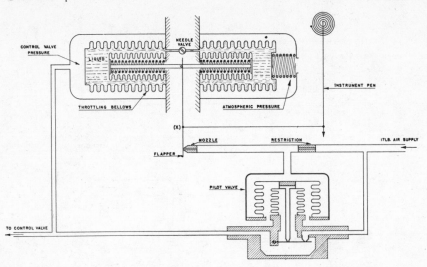

Fig. 70 - Schematic Diagram of Brown Air-O-Line Controller
with Automatic Reset
Courtesy of Brown Instrument Company

right-hand internal spring has been compressed, and the left-hand
internal spring has been extended. Therefore, the pressure on the
fluid in the right-hand bellows is greater than the fluid pressure
in the left-hand bellows. Naturally, the liquid tends to flow from
the right-hand bellows through the needle valve to the left-hand
bellows. As this occurs, the smaller inner bellows tend to return
to their original positions. This actuates the baffle, nozzle,
and relay valve again to reduce the output pressure from the controller so that the small bellows and their internal springs are
kept in this same position. Now, as long as the pen on the instrument remains away from the set pointer, this action continues at a
rate which is proportional to the deviation. It will be recalled
that this meets the definition of automatic reset response. As
soon as the pen returns to the control point, the small bellows
and the compression springs return to their original position, but
the larger bellows will have assumed a new position, such that the
compression in the large helical spring at the right is considerably less. The system is again in equilibrium, and yet the pen has
returned substantially to the control point. The throttling range
may be adjusted as with the full throttling controller from 1 to
150% of chart range, while the reset rate may be adjusted through
a wide range by means of the needle valve in the liquid line connecting the two larger bellows.

Fig. 71 is a cutaway photograph of the Brown Air-O-Line Controller. In this particular instrument, the actuating element is
located in the upper right-hand corner of the case. The sensitivity
dial calibrated in throttling range and the automatic reset dial

Information Sheet 7

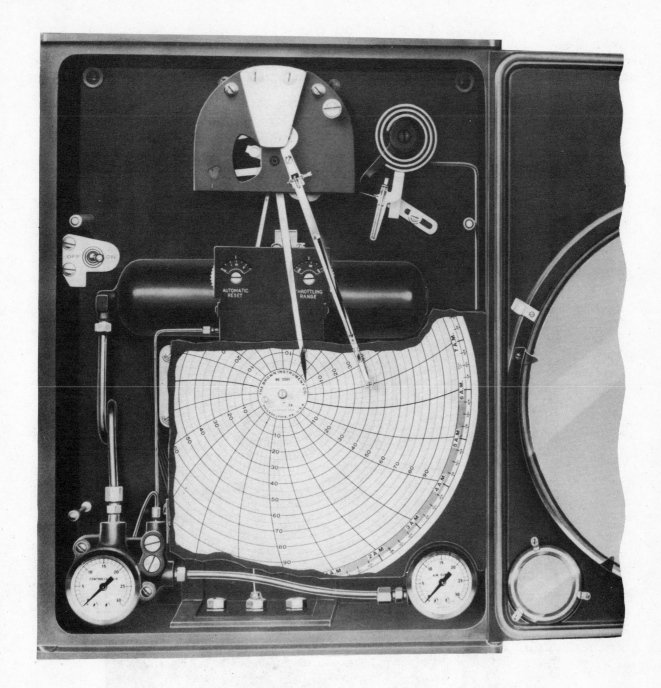

Fig. 71 - Cut-Away View of Brown Air-O-Line Controller with
Automatic Reset

Courtesy of Brown Instrument Company

are located directly above the center of the chart. It will be
noted that in this instrument, both of these control effects are
continuously adjustable through their full range. The pressure
gages are located in the lower corners of the case, and the

Information Sheet 7

non-bleed pilot valve is situated directly behind the gage in the lower left-hand corner. Possibly the salient features of this particular instrument are the non-bleed pilot valve and the liquid damping system used to obtain the automatic reset response.

Fig. 72 - Brown Air-O-Line Controller
Courtesy of Brown Instrument Company

Fig. 72 shows the same instrument with the outer cover and chart in place.

Information Sheet 7

The Bristol Free-Vane Controller

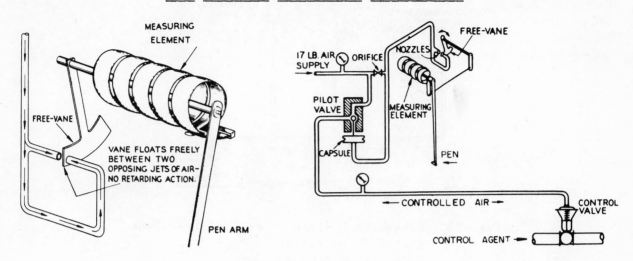

Fig. 73 - Bristol Free-Vane Control   Fig. 74 - Schematic Diagram of Bristol
         Mechanism   Free-Vane Monoset Controller

Courtesy of Bristol Company

The Bristol Company manufactures a series of controllers which have many features in common with those discussed previously. The outstanding feature of these Bristol instruments is the free-vane principle, and this can best be explained by referring to Figs. 73 and 74.

Fig. 73 is a drawing of the free-vane control mechanism. In the Monoset Controller, illustrated in Fig. 73, the Bourdon tube is connected by suitable linkage to a small stainless steel vane which is pivoted in such a manner that it can be swung by the Bourdon tube between two opposing nozzles. The nozzles are fed from the instrument air supply through an orifice. The gap between the nozzles is approximately .007" and as the free-vane swings in to close the nozzles, the nozzle back pressure increases. This change in back pressure is amplified through the usual ball type relay valve, and the output from the controller is applied to a control valve. The set point on the controller is adjusted by shifting the nozzle location so that the edge of the vane passes between the nozzle at different temperatures. Control action always occurs when the vane is just entering or leaving the gap between the nozzles.

It will be noted that with this double nozzle and vane principle, the Bourdon tube can move the vane freely when the nozzle back pressure is high as well as when it is low. This differs from the baffle and nozzle combination illustrated in Fig. 29 since in these figures the baffle movement must stop after the nozzle is closed. Since the vane swings between two opposed nozzles, the detent in this instrument is small. The Monoset Controller has a throttling range of from 1 to 100% of chart travel.

Information Sheet 7

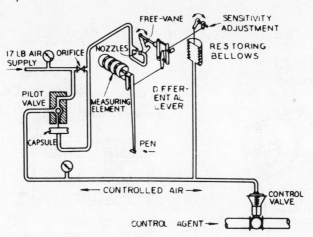

Fig. 75 - Schematic Diagram of Bristol Free-Vane
Ampliset Controller
Courtesy of Bristol Company

Fig. 75 is a schematic diagram of the Bristol Ampliset Controller. This instrument uses pneumatic sensitivity reduction and while the method of adjusting the sensitivity is not shown, it is accomplished by changing the length of the levers in the system between the restoring bellows and the free vane.

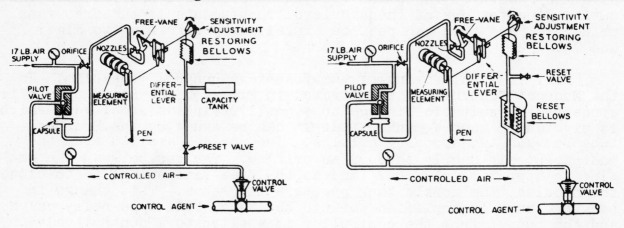

Fig. 76 - Schematic Diagram of Bristol
Free-Vane Preset Controller

Fig. 77 - Schematic Diagram of Bristol
Free-Vane Reset Controller

Courtesy of Bristol Company

Fig. 76 illustrates the Bristol Preset Controller in which the rate response effect is accomplished by means of a needle valve in the line to the sensitivity reducing bellows. This is the same system that is used in the Taylor Pre-Act Controller.

Referring to Fig. 77, it may be seen that the automatic reset feature is incorporated in the Bristol controller in a slightly different manner. The output pressure from the

Information Sheet 7

controller is connected to the outside of a bellows which under
equilibrium conditions has atmospheric pressure on its inside.
The inside of the bellows is connected by a tube to a second bellows (restoring bellows) which operates through the linkage to
reduce the controller sensitivity. The pressure in the line
between the two bellows is vented to the atmosphere through a
needle valve. Assuming that the Bourdon tube moves the free-vane
between the nozzles to increase the back pressure, the output
pressure from the controller decreases.

This reduced pressure on the outside of the lower bellows
causes it to expand, reducing the pressure within the bellows,
the restoring bellows and the connecting tubing. The pressure
in the system, consisting of the two bellows and connecting tubing, at this time is below atmospheric. The upper bellows contracts and through the lever system cancels a portion of the
movement of the free-vane. This is the sensitivity reducing action.

Now, since the needle valve connecting the inside of the two
bellows to the atmosphere is partially open, the internal pressure
gradually approaches atmospheric. As this occurs, the original
sensitivity reduction is gradually cancelled and automatic reset
is obtained.

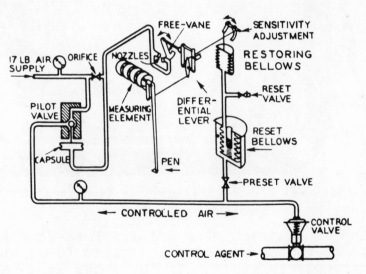

Fig. 78 - Schematic Diagram of Bristol Free-Vane
Magniset Controller
Courtesy of Bristol Company

The Bristol instrument incorporating both rate and reset
responses is illustrated in Fig. 78. It is called the Magniset
Controller.

Information Sheet 7

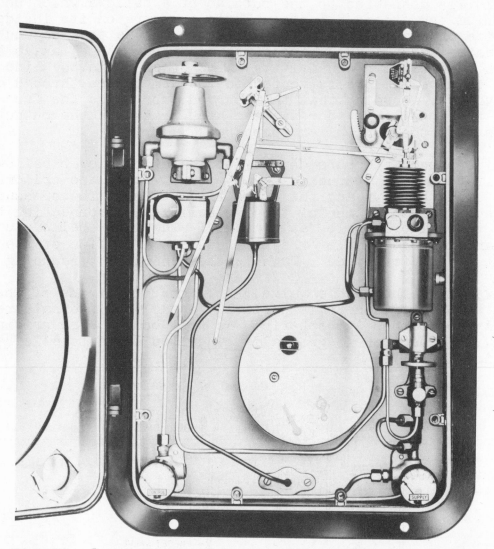

Fig. 79 - Internal View of Bristol Free-Vane Feset Controller
Courtesy of Bristol Company

Fig. 79 is a photograph of a Bristol Free-Vane Reset Controller with the chart and plate removed. The valve for controlling the instrument air supply is located in the upper left-hand corner of the case. A manual-automatic switch is directly below this valve. The small knob in the upper right-hand corner of the case is the control point adjustment knob, and in the extreme upper right-hand corner, provision is made to adjust the instrument sensitivity.

Directly beneath the sensitivity adjustment and its linkage is the sensitivity reducing bellows, and beneath these bellows is the needle valve adjusting knob. The cylindrical container beneath the knob is a housing for the lower bellows so that the output

Information Sheet 7

pressure may be applied to the outside of these bellows. Beneath
this cylindrical housing is the air relay valve and in the lower
right-hand corner of the case is the air supply gage. The air output gage is located in the lower left-hand corner of the case.
This particular instrument is illustrated with an electric clock,
located in the lower center of the case.

Fig. 80 - Bristol Free-Vane Preset Controller
Courtesy of Bristol Company

Fig. 80 is a view of the Bristol Free-Vane Preset Controller
with the chart and plate in place.

Information Sheet 7

The Tagliabue Air-Operated Controller

The Tagliabue Company manufactures a series of controllers which are competitive with those which have been described previously.

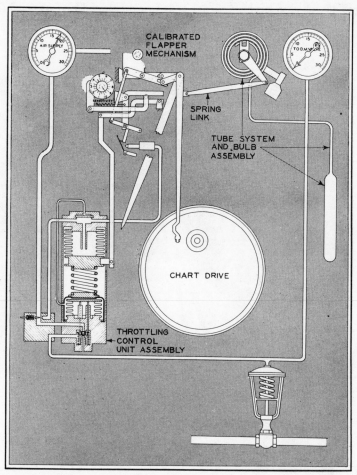

CALIBRATED
FLAPPER
MECHANISM

SPRING
LINK

TUBE SYSTEM
AND BULB
ASSEMBLY

CHART DRIVE

THROTTLING
CONTROL
UNIT ASSEMBLY

Fig. 81 - Schematic Diagram of Tag High Sensitivity Controller
Courtesy of C.J. Tagliabue Mfg. Company

Fig. 81 is a schematic diagram of the Tag High Sensitivity (On-Off) Controller. The Bourdon tube operates the pen arm which in turn operates the baffle through a series of levers. The instrument has the direct set feature and a knurled knob is provided for adjusting the position of the set pointer. The instrument may be changed from direct to reverse-acting by simply disconnecting the link fastened to the T-shaped crank and moving it over to the other end of the crank. Provision is made in this instrument to change the sensitivity mechanically by varying the relationship between the movement of the T-shaped crank and the baffle. It will be seen that the sensitivity adjustment is accomplished without pneumatic sensitivity reduction, and it is limited at the low end to a throttling range of 15% of chart travel. The sensitivity adjustment is continuous, and it is accomplished by a knurled knob.

Information Sheet 7

The air supply is connected through an orifice to the nozzle and the nozzle back pressure affects a bellows which operates a ball type relay valve. The output pressure from the controller depends upon the position of the ball in the relay valve with respect to the supply and exhaust ports, and, therefore, this relay valve bleeds air from the system continuously. Unlike the Bristol and Taylor relay valves, this valve is direct-acting, since a high nozzle back pressure results in a high output pressure.

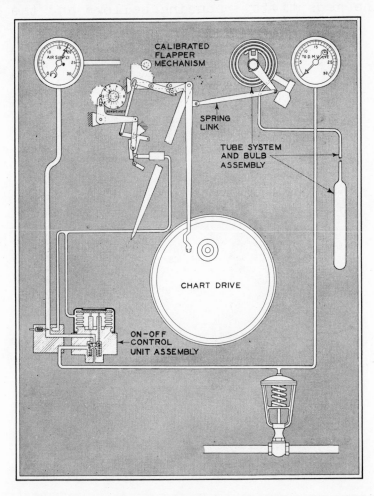

Fig. 82 - Schematic Diagram of Tag Full Range Throttling Controller
Courtesy of C.J. Tagliabue Mfg. Company

The Tagliabue Full Range Throttling Controller is illustrated in Fig. 82. A bellows has been added to the line connecting the orifice to the nozzle. This operates the baffle in order to reduce the instrument sensitivity. Assuming that the Bourdon tube moves the pen and lever system in such a way that the baffle tends to close the nozzle, this new bellows expands against a spring and pulls down a connecting link, which, through an arrangement of levers, moves the baffle away from the nozzle. Thus, when this additional

Information Sheet 7

bellows and spring are in the circuit, a considerably greater motion of the Bourdon tube is required to open and close the nozzle.

This type of sensitivity reduction is somewhat different from that described previously in that the nozzle back pressure, rather than the output pressure from the relay valve, is used for this purpose. In this instrument, the sensitivity is adjusted by a knurled knob which operates to change the relationship between the movement of the sensitivity reducing bellows and the baffle.

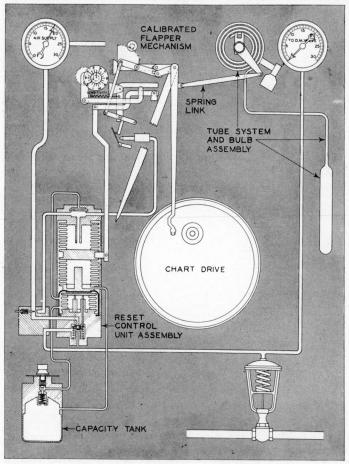

Fig. 83 - Schematic Diagram of Tag Full Range Throttling
Controller with Automatic Reset
Courtesy of C.J. Tagliabue Mfg. Company

The Tagliabue instrument incorporating automatic reset is illustrated in Fig. 83. In this instrument, the pneumatic sensitivity reducing action is gradually cancelled by an additional bellows. This bellows is connected to the line connecting the orifice and the nozzle through an adjustable needle valve. The opening of this needle valve determines the reset rate. As is the case with the Full Range Throttling Controller, this instrument utilizes the nozzle back pressure to obtain the sensitivity reducing action and the automatic reset action.

Information Sheet 7

Fig. 84 - Cut-Away View of Tag Full Range Throttling Controller
with Automatic Reset
Courtesy of C.J. Tagliabue Mfg. Company

Fig. 84 is a cut-away photograph of the Tagliabue Full Range
Throttling Controller with automatic reset.

The control point adjustment knob is just to the right of
the air supply gage, which is located in the upper left-hand corner. The sensitivity adjustment knob is directly below this same
gage. The instrument is provided with a continuous sensitivity
adjustment.

The Bourdon tube is located directly to the left of the output
pressure gage in the upper right-hand corner. The needle valve,
governing the rate of reset, is in the lower left-hand corner with
the relay valve and orifice located directly above it. The sensitivity reducing bellows and automatic reset bellows are housed in
the cylindrical container.

Information Sheet 8   THE CONTROL VALVE AND VALVE POSITIONER

The theory of control has been discussed, but no great attention has been focused on the control valve. The control valve is accepted as part of the process - and rightly so. However, it is at the same time a part of the control system and it is necessary to consider the valve as to its construction, operation and characteristics. The selection of the proper valve is not difficult, but the use of an improper valve can be the downfall of a good control system.

We know that automatic control has replaced manual control in many processes. In these, the controller now positions the valve that the operator formerly positioned. The valve, actuated by a controller, is of somewhat different construction than the valve adjusted by the operator.

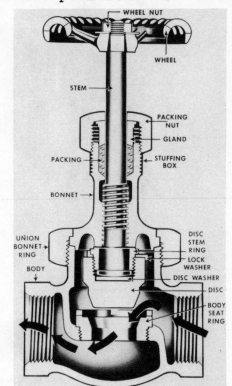

Let us compare the construction of these two valve types. Figs. 85 and 86 show cross-sections of a nand valve and a control valve respectively. The operator positions the hand valve by turning the handle. The stem of this valve has been threaded so that turning it clockwise closes the valve, and turning it counter-clockwise opens it. Thus, for every movement of the hand-wheel, there is a corresponding upward or downward movement of the valve disc. The control valve, Fig. 86, has no threaded valve stem. The valve stem in this case is easily pushed in or pulled out to regulate the valve disc. A diaphragm motor is used to position and hold the valve disc at the desired location. This is accomplished as follows:

Fig. 85 - Cross-Sectional View of
A Hand Valve

Courtesy of Crane Company

1. The valve stem is attached to the diaphragm motor push-rod.
2. Air output of the controller enters the motor through the air inlet port.
3. An increase in controller output pressure acts against the rubber diaphragm, forcing the push-rod downward.
4. The push-rod is forced downward compressing the spring, until the force in the compressed spring plus the unbalanced force due to line pressure equals the force on the rubber diaphragm.
5. When the air pressure in the motor top decreases, the spring forces the push-rod upward.
6. Thus, for every pressure output of a controller, there is a definite valve position.

Information Sheet 8

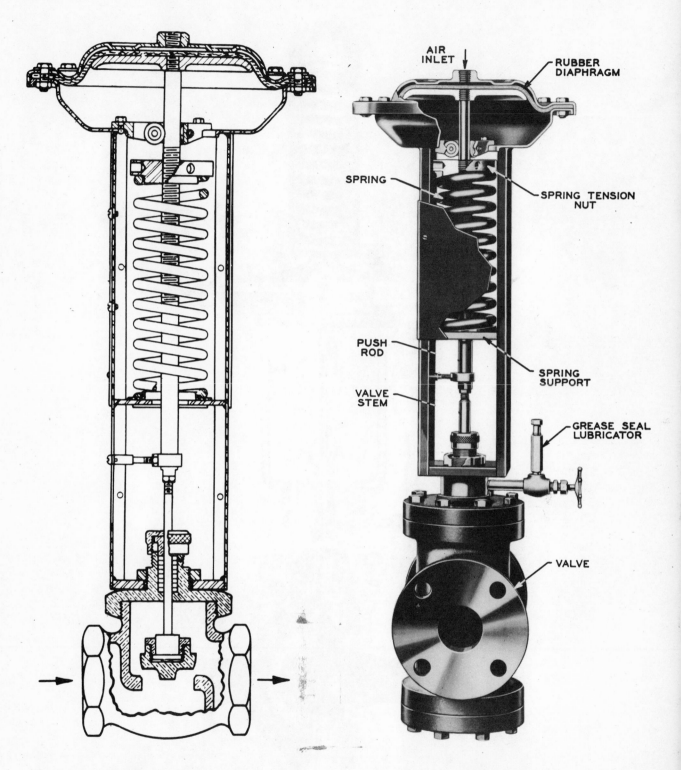

Fig. 86 - Cross-Sectional View of a
Diaphragm Motor and Valve

Fig. 87 - Cut-Away View of a Diaphragm
Motor and Valve

Courtesy of Taylor Instrument Companies

Information Sheet 8

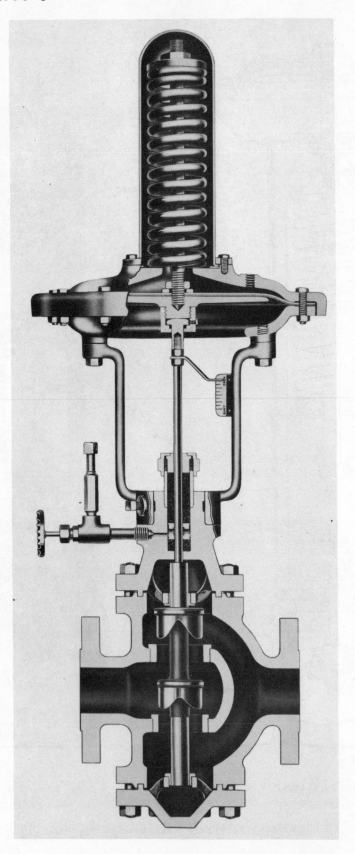

Fig. 88 - Another Type Motor and Valve
Courtesy of Foxboro Company

Information Sheet 8

Control from either type of valve is dependent upon changing the position of the valve disc, adjusting the opening to correct the quantity of flow. The only difference in the two valves is the method of moving the valve disc.

While the operation of a standard control valve is as simple as outlined above, care must be exercised to insure that the correct valve for a given job is installed.

Fig. 88 shows another type of diaphragm motor and valve construction. Notice the guides on the valve plunger and the absence of guides on the motor push-rod.

Valve Action

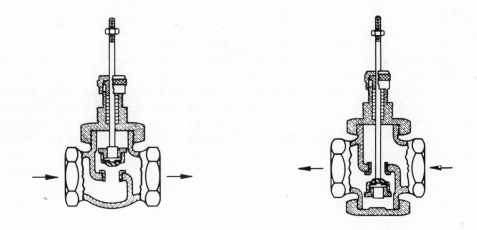

Fig. 89 - An Air-to-Close
Valve

Fig. 90 - An Air-to-Open
Valve

Courtesy of Taylor Instrument Companies

A general classification of valves is made according to the method of opening and closing. A valve which is closed by the application of air pressure is called an air-to-close valve, Fig. 89, and one which is opened by the application of air pressure is called an air-to-open valve, Fig. 90.

There is a definite need for both types of valves. Let us consider a cooling application where we are controlling the flow of cooling water to maintain a constant temperature. If the air supply to the diaphragm motor failed, we would want the valve on the cooling water to stay open and protect the equipment from over-heating. An air-to-close valve would be installed on this application. Should we have a heating application where steam flow is being controlled, it is essential that the control valve close on air failure to protect the process from over-heating. An installation of this nature would require an air-to-open valve.

Information Sheet 8

Seat Arrangement

Control valves may be supplied with either a single or double seat. Figs. 89 and 90 are single seated valves, while Fig. 91 is a double seated valve. Single seated valves are used where the pressure drop across the valve is small, the line pressure does not fluctuate and where periods of complete shut-off against low upstream pressures are desired. On applications using single seated valves with high pressure drops and high line pressures, extremely large motors would be needed for control and shut-off. Also, if the line pressure fluctuated widely, excessive control point deviations would result.

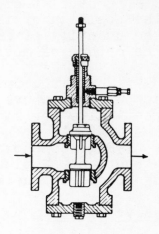

Fig. 91 - A Double Seated Bevel
Disc Valve

Courtesy of Taylor Instrument Cos.

Single seated valves should be installed so that the incoming flow tends to force the valve open, Figs. 89 and 90. In an air-to-close valve, the line pressure would act against the air pressure on the diaphragm, while in an air-to-open valve the spring would resist the line pressure. Installations are made in this manner to obtain good control. If the flow through the valve were reversed, then as the valve disc approached its seat the pressure drop across the valve would increase, forcing the disc against its seat. Under these conditions, the valve would be unstable and throttling control could not be obtained.

Double seated valves are used in larger sizes for higher pressure drops and where complete shut-off is not required. Also, on applications with fluctuating pressure, a double seated valve, Fig. 91, is generally preferred. The line pressures enter these valves between the discs, and they are partially balanced. This feature reduces, to a great extent, the effect of varying line pressures, and a reasonably constant valve position can be maintained in spite of these fluctuations. The semi-balanced feature also permits operation at high pressure drops through the valve because the forces generated by the diaphragm motor do not have to overcome the full force created by the line pressure acting on one disc, as is the case in a single-seated valve. Larger valves can also be operated without resorting to excessively large diaphragm motors.

The lift or valve stem travel of a double-seated valve is less than that of an equivalent sized single-seated valve.

Both valve discs are rigidly connected and move as a unit. Since there are two seating surfaces, it is extremely difficult to have both discs seat tightly, simultaneously. For this reason, double seated valves rarely produce a tight shut-off. Unless the

Information Sheet 8

valves are ground in very carefully at the operating temperature
and the seating surfaces wear uniformly, they cannot be relied upon
to give tight shut-off.

The flow per unit lift of double-seated valves is necessarily
greater than that of corresponding single-seated valves. Hence,
in the smaller sizes the flow per unit lift presents a greater
percentage of the total flow capacity. In order to obtain satisfactory performance at low lifts at a reasonable cost, it is
recommended that the use of double-seated valves in sizes less than
1" be avoided.

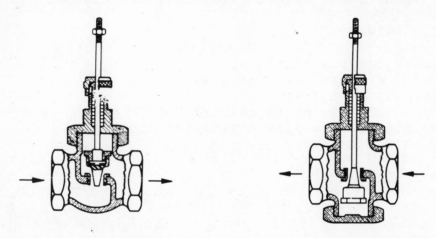

Fig. 92 - Air-to-Close   Fig. 93 - Air-to-Open
        Needle Valve   Needle Valve

Courtesy of Taylor Instrument Companies

Where accurate control is required in these smaller sizes,
needle valves may be used. The air-to-open and air-to-close types
are illustrated in Figs. 92 and 93

A control valve should have its operating range within the
range of the controller actuating it. For illustrative purposes
assume that a controller has an output pressure range of 0-20 psi,
then the valve should have a range of approximately 3-15 psi. This
insures complete opening and closing. If this is an air-to-close
valve and the line pressure has increased slightly - so that it
takes 17 psi to close the valve - the instrument has sufficient power to do it. If the valve was air-to-open, the initial compression
in the spring insures that the spring will close the valve. A
variety of springs sufficient to meet the needs of most operating
conditions is available. The initial starting point of movement
(2,3 or 4 psi), for a valve can be changed by moving the spring
adjusting nut, Fig. 87. The initial compression of the spring is
then changed, but the range is not shortened. For example, if a
diaphragm motor with a 3-15 psi range is adjusted to start at 5 psi,

Information Sheet 8

then the new overall range would be 5-17 psi. When the starting
point of the diaphragm motor is changed, always be sure the spring
coils do not go metal to metal before the valve reaches the end of
its stroke. Increasing the initial compression of the spring short-
ens the distance between coils, and sometimes limits the stroke of
the push-rod.

Characteristics

For purposes of description, valves may be classed as bevel
disc valves or characterized valves. The following is a brief summary of pertinent facts relating to these two classes:

Bevel disc valves

1. Require careful sizing.
2. Provide greater maximum flow.
3. Generally cost less.
4. Are usually easier to maintain.
5. Have linear flow-lift characteristics up to 50%
   of their total travel.

Characterized valves

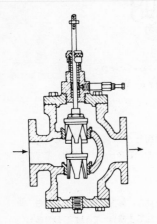 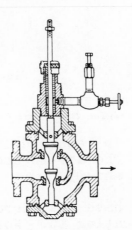 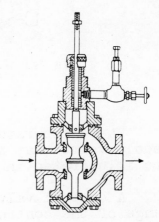

Fig. 94 - Double Seated　　Fig. 95 - Double Seated　　Fig. 96 - Double Seated
　　V-Port Valve　　　　　　Throttle Plug Valve　　　　Ratio Plug Valve

Courtesy of Taylor Instrument Companies

1. Various disc contours have been used in an attempt to get
   equal percentages of flow change for equal increments of
   valve lift. Valves of this type are known as characterized
   or percentage type valves. Figs. 94, 95 and 96 show some
   of these valves in the air-to-close type. They are also
   available in the air-to-open type.

Information Sheet 8

2. On some applications characterized valves make it unnecessary to readjust the controller sensitivity for large load
changes.

*Note: Change of controller sensitivity may be necessitated not only
by load changes but also by time lag and other process characteristics.*

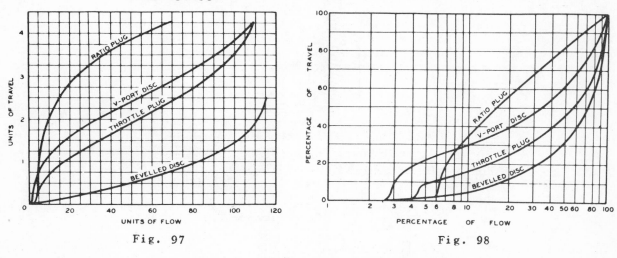

Fig. 97   Fig. 98

Courtesy of Taylor Instrument Companies

Fig. 97 gives the flow lift characteristics for several types
of valves. In general, the better valve for a given application
is the one with the most linear characteristics throughout its
operating range. Another factor to consider is the importance of
accurate control for small values of valve opening.

Fig. 98 shows the percentage of valve travel plotted against
the percentage of flow on a semi-logarithmic scale.

Saunders Patent Valve

The Saunders patent non-metallic diaphragm
disc type valve, Fig. 99, is particularly applicable in the chemical and allied fields because
it is of the packless type. It is easily dis-
mantled for cleaning, making it desirable for
use with acids, alkalies, food products, petroleum products and gases, such as Freon or
Carrene.

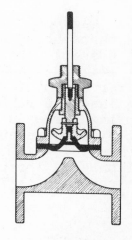

Fig. 99 - Saunders Type
Valve
Courtesy of Taylor Instrument Cos.

Information Sheet 8

Hand Wheel for Manual Valve Operation

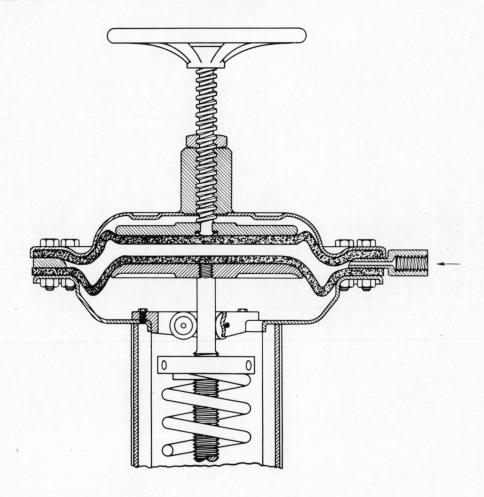

Fig. 100 - Cross-Sectional View of Diaphragm Valve with
Hand Wheel Adjustment

Fig: 100 illustrates a hand wheel attached to a screw, threaded through the top plate of a diaphragm motor. This device makes
it possible to operate the valve manually in case of air failure
or if manual adjustments are desirable for any other reason. The
lower end of the threaded stem engages a push-plate which acts
against the rubber diaphragm and moves the push-rod against the
spring force just as the air pressure does during ordinary operation. To prevent leakage of air past the threads, two diaphragms
are used. Air to operate the motor is admitted between the rubber
diaphragms through the port in the dual connecting ring. A locknut
is provided to fix the disc position.

Information Sheet 8

Butterfly Valves

Butterfly valves are sometimes used on applications where
the flow consists of pulpy, viscous or semi-solid material and
for gas and air to or from large
apparatus, such as burners and
furnaces.

They are constructed for
operating pressures up to 400
psi and temperatures to 900°F.
They can be supplied with radial
thrust bearings, ball bearings,
radiating fins, grease seal stem
lubricators, or rotary shaft,
stem position indicators.

Butterfly valves are made
in sizes from 3/4" to 36" in
diameter. Valves smaller than
2" are fitted with screwed stuffing boxes while valves larger
than 2" have bolted gland stuffing boxes. A typical butterfly
valve with diaphragm motor and
positioner is shown in Fig. 101.

Fig. 101 - Butterfly Valve with Diaphragm, Motor and Positioner
Courtesy of Taylor Instrument Companies

Information Sheet 8

Louvre Damper

Fig. 102 - A Louvre Damper with Motor
Courtesy of Foxboro Company

Fig. 102 shows a type of louvre damper construction which is frequently used for the control of air flow in air conditioning systems. An application of these valves is shown in Information Sheet 14.

96

Information Sheet 8

Grease Seal Lubricator

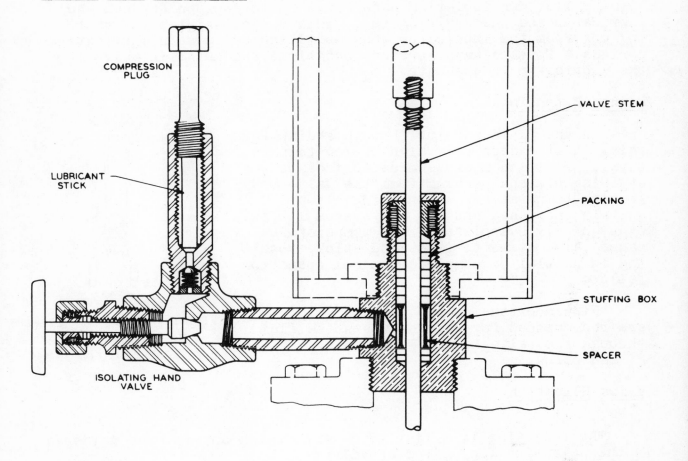

COMPRESSION PLUG

LUBRICANT STICK

ISOLATING HAND VALVE

VALVE STEM

PACKING

STUFFING BOX

SPACER

Fig. 103

A factor contributing to the hysteresis of diaphragm valves is the friction in the stuffing box due to the pressure of the packing against the valve stem. Grease seal lubricators provide an effective means of minimizing this difficulty as well as helping to reduce stem leakage.

A few hours after a freshly packed valve is put into operation a portion of the lubricant is expelled from the packing. Because this surplus lubricant has been lost, a slight leakage may occur at the stem, making further tightening necessary. After this, however, the packing pressure and lubricant density film will have reached a balance and the maximum service will be obtained.

When more lubricant is needed, it is applied in stick form. The lubricant stick is inserted beneath the compression plug which forces the lubricant around the spacer which separates the packing into two parts. This permits the lubricant to work both ways and provides an effective seal and adequate lubrication. See Fig. 103.

Information Sheet 8

For high temperature and pressure applications requiring cast steel valves, an isolating hand valve is interposed between the lubricator and the stuffing box. This valve isolates the stuffing box from the lubricator when refilling or between lubricating periods. For ordinary service conditions the built-in valve in the lubricator is adequate.

Finned Extensions

If the fluid passing through a diaphragm valve is at excessively high or low temperatures, provision must be made to isolate the stuffing box and packing from the valve body. At high temperatures the packing life is greatly shortened and the valve stem lubricant quickly evaporates. Low temperatures cause valve stems to frost and stick, resulting in partial or complete control operation failure.

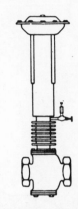

Fig. 104 - Finned Extension Type Diaphragm Valve
Courtesy of Taylor Instrument Cos.

Finned extension type valves, Fig. 104, are recommended for service where the fluid through the valve is 450°F. and over, or 20° F. and below.

Valve Selection

The following is a list of factors which should be considered in the selection and sizing of valves:

1. Reliable mechanical construction.

2. Ease of maintenance.

3. Resistance to erosion.

4. Use of air-to-open or air-to-close, considering safety in case of air failure.

5. The valve should be sized so that its operating range lies within the linear portion of its characteristic curve.

6. On continuous processes, it is recommended practice that the valve be one size smaller than the line. The effect of the restriction caused by an undersized line is shown clearly by Fig. 105.

Information Sheet 8

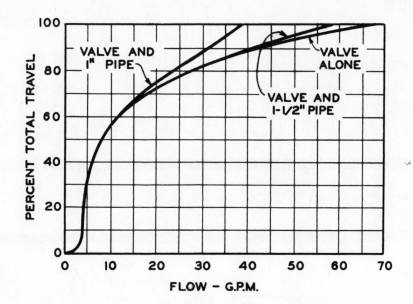

Fig. 105 - Effect on Flow-Lift Characteristics Using
30 ft. of 1 in. or 1-½ in. pipe with 1 in.
Ratio Plug Valve.

Courtesy of Taylor Instrument Companies

7. On valves 2" and larger the use of a double seated valve
   is indicated since its position is practically unaffected
   by changes in upstream pressure. Less force is required
   to operate this valve and it will move through a shorter
   stroke, hence a smaller diaphragm motor may be used.

8. Double seated valves are not recommended where a tight
   shut-off is required.

After proper selection and sizing of a valve, it must be properly installed and maintained. The control valve should always be
the 'bottle neck' for flow, being installed in a line at least one
size larger than itself. If this is not done, it will be found
that the effect of the last half of the valve opening is very limited,
with serious upsetting effects.

Unless the process can be shut down for valve repairs, a by-
pass should be provided around the control valve. The valve motor
air line should be of adequate size as specified by the instrument
manufacturer.

Fig. 106 shows a valve selector slide rule, which also is arranged with a set of scales on the back of the slide for use in
estimating flow meter orifice, nozzle, venturi and pipe size.

Information Sheet 8

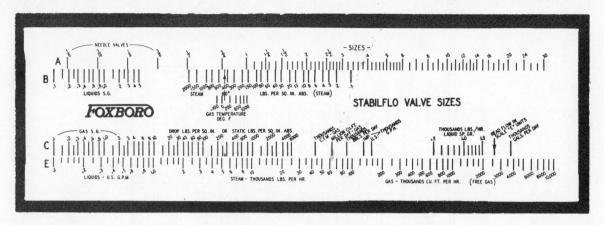

Face of the Valve Selector Slide Rule

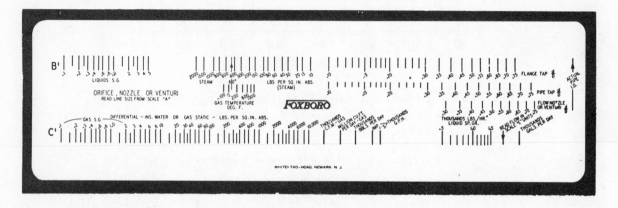

Orifice, Nozzle and Venturi Scales on Reverse of Slide

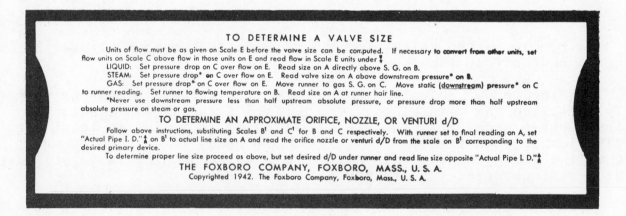

Back of the Valve Selector Slide Rule

Fig. 106

Courtesy of Foxboro Company

The slide rule, Fig. 106, or valve selector charts, Figs. 107, 108 and 109 aid in the selection of the correct size and type of valve.

Information Sheet 8

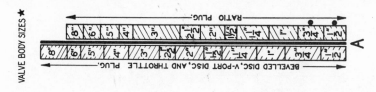

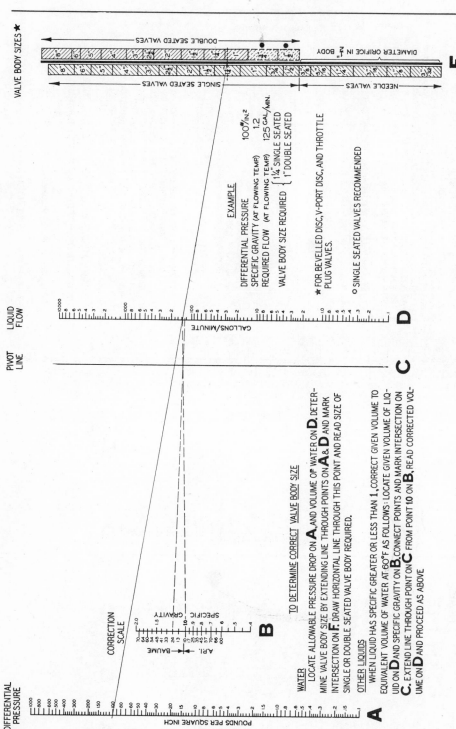

Fig. 107 - Valve Selector Chart for Liquids

Courtesy of Taylor Instrument Companies

Information Sheet 8

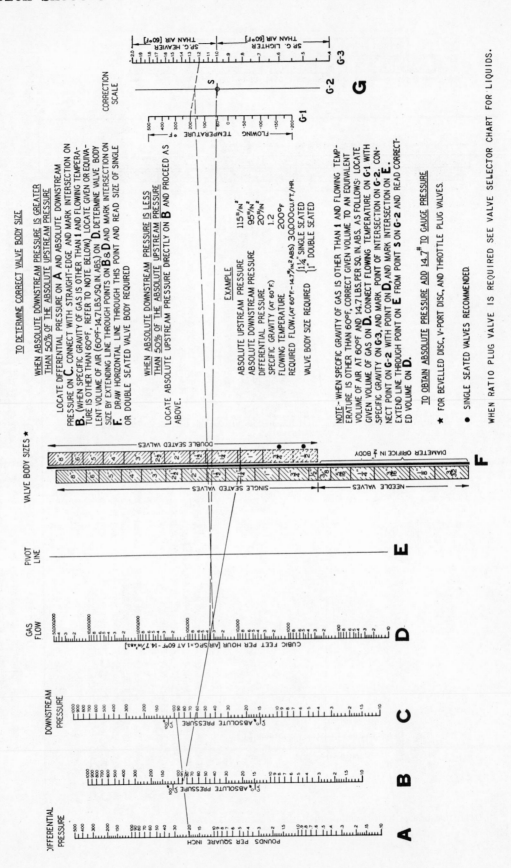

Fig. 108 - Valve Selector Chart for Steam
Courtesy of Taylor Instrument Companies

Information Sheet 8

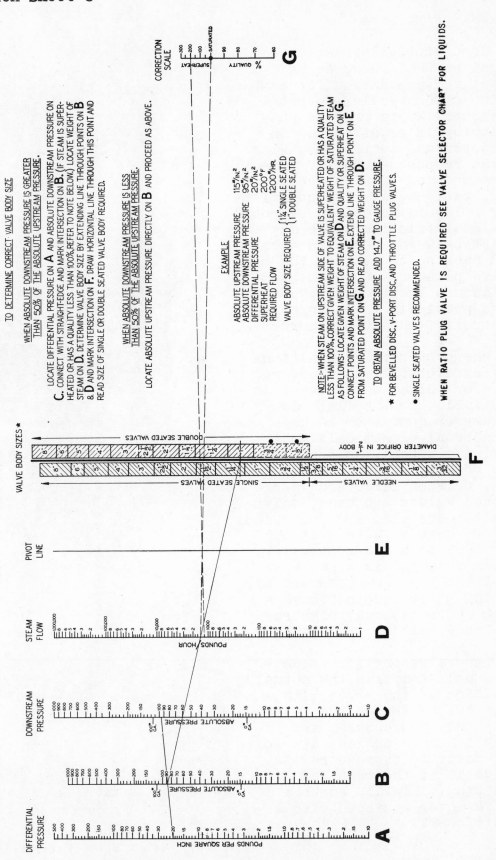

Fig. 109 - Valve Selector Chart for Gases
Courtesy of Taylor Instrument Companies

Information Sheet 8

Valve Positioners

Good controller action requires that there be an exact valve position for each value of controller output pressure. Where precise positioning is required, as on proportional controllers with reset response--usually temperature and liquid level applications, a valve positioning relay is needed to overcome residual friction which may exist between the valve stem and packing or between the valve plunger and ports, and to assure that the valve follows precisely the changes of controller output pressure.

Where operating conditions are unfavorable, as where no safe or suitable lubricant is available, or the fluid is sticky or gummy, or leakage of corrosive chemicals must positively be avoided by the use of very tight valve packing, or when large single seated valves are used, valve positioners also are justified. Also, where a valve must be far away from its controller, quick response is aided by a positioner as low pressure air to the motor does not have a long and relatively high resistance path to travel.

The valve positioner continuously compares the actual position of the valve with that called for by the instrument output pressure, and supplies more or less air to the motor as is required to drive it to the required position. Fig.110 shows a valve motor equipped with a positioner.

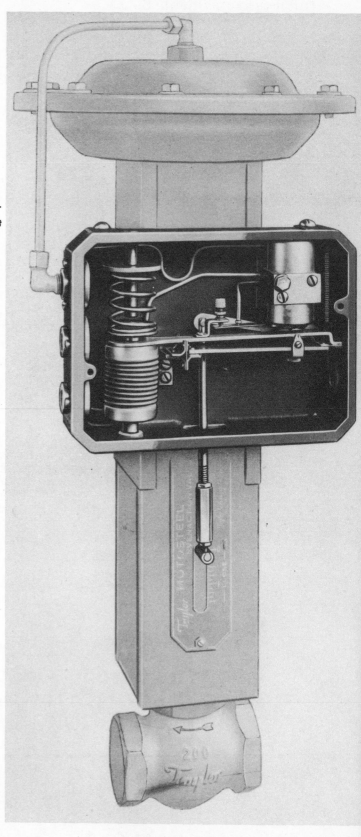

Fig. 110 - Valve Motor With Positioner
Courtesy of Taylor Instrument Companies

Information Sheet 8

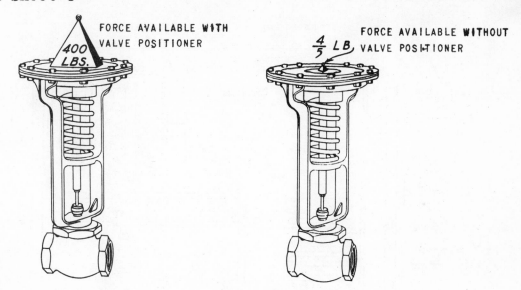

Fig. 111 - The Advantage of Using a Valve Positioner
Courtesy of Taylor Instrument Companies

Fig. 111 illustrates the advantage of the valve positioner in bringing the full pressure of the air supply source to act upon the diaphragm valve, rather than the reduced force which would be exerted by the controller output pressure.

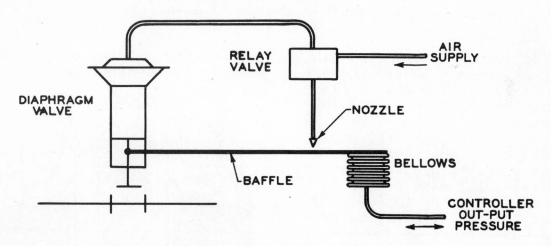

Fig. 112 - Schematic Diagram Showing the Operation of a
Valve Positioner

Fig. 112 is a schematic diagram showing the operation of one type of valve positioner. Notice that the combined effect of the controller output pressure and the position of the diaphragm valve stem determines the position of the baffle. When the baffle is close to the nozzle, the relay valve operates to admit air supply, but when the baffle is away from the nozzle, the relay valve bleeds air from the diaphragm chamber, allowing the valve to open.

Information Sheet 8

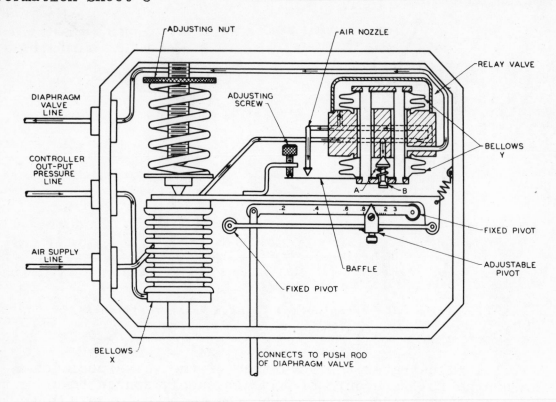

ADJUSTING NUT

AIR NOZZLE

RELAY VALVE

DIAPHRAGM
VALVE
LINE

ADJUSTING
SCREW

BELLOWS
Y

CONTROLLER
OUT-PUT
PRESSURE
LINE

A   B

.2   .4   .6 .8 2 3

FIXED PIVOT

AIR SUPPLY
LINE

BAFFLE

ADJUSTABLE
PIVOT

FIXED PIVOT

BELLOWS
X

CONNECTS TO PUSH ROD
OF DIAPHRAGM VALVE

Fig. 113 - Schematic Diagram of a Valve Positioner
Courtesy of Taylor Instrument Companies

The schematic diagram, Fig. 113, shows more of the details of
this positioner. Should there be a drop in the controller output
pressure, bellows X will deflate,
and the adjusting screw resting
against the flexible baffle will
move the baffle away from the
nozzle. Likewise, should the controller output pressure increase,
the baffle will move closer to
the nozzle. In the latter case,
examination of the relay valve
in the upper right of the positioner shows that placing the
baffle close to the nozzle will
increase the back pressure above
the upper bellows, forcing the
bellows unit downward and moving
plunger A away from the air supply opening.

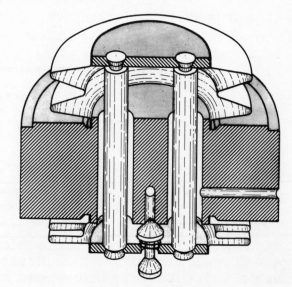

Fig. 114 - Details of Construction of
the Relay Valve

106

Information Sheet 8

This will permit the full air supply pressure to go directly to the tube leading to the diaphragm valve line.

Fig. 114 shows more of the details of the construction of the relay valve.

Air pressure admitted to the diaphragm motor imparts a downward motion to the valve stem and push-rod. The rod shown at the bottom of the figure is attached to the valve push-rod; hence it is moved downward. See Fig. 113.

The linkage to which this rod attaches is supported as follows: the left end of the lower arm is attached to a fixed pivot. At the right, this arm is attached to the long bellows supported arm. Here the position of the two arms is regulated somewhat by means of a small spring which exerts an upward tension.

The center arm which connects directly to the rod is pivoted at its extreme right on a pin supported by the housing. The effect of its movement is modified by means of the adjustable pivot.

The downward motion of the valve stem then causes the right end of the linkage to move downward. This moves the baffle away from the nozzle and the system thus regains equilibrium.

Should the controller output pressure decrease, bellows X will be deflated and the baffle will be moved away from the nozzle. This will reduce the pressure above the upper bellows, causing the bellows unit to move upward, carrying plunger A with it. This closes the air supply opening, and as the bellows unit continues to rise, air is released beneath the plunger at point B, thereby releasing air from the diaphragm chamber. Fig. 114 shows a sectional view of the relay valve in this position. As this air is released, the valve stem and push-rod rise, lifting the right end of the baffle positioning arm until the baffle is again at a position of equilibrium with respect to the nozzle.

The adjustable pivot may be set to limit the travel of the valve stem as indicated by the graduations. The scale for the adjustable pivot reads in inches of valve travel.

The operating range of the precisor may be shifted by turning the adjusting nut at the upper left of the figure. This range may also be lengthened or shortened by changing springs. A relatively light spring will give more valve action for smaller pressure variations; hence it will operate over a shorter pressure range. This refers only to the operating pressures for the precisor and should not be confused with the operating pressures for the valve.

Information Sheet 8

    When the baffle is positioned at the correct distance from the nozzle, the system is in equilibrium and no movement of the valve results. Any change of this positioning actuates the relay valve which operates to inflate or deflate the diaphragm motor by means of the independent source of air pressure.

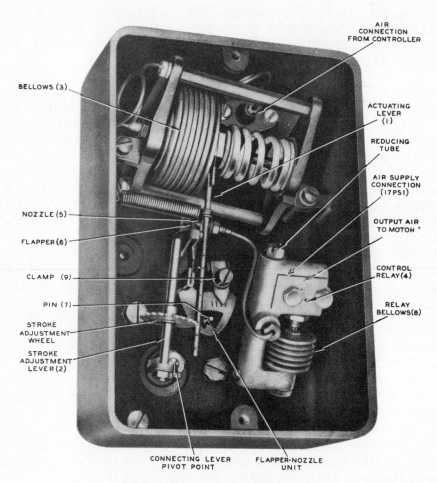

Fig. 115 - A Valve Positioner
Courtesy of Foxboro Company

    Fig. 115 illustrates another valve positioner of this type. Assuming a decrease in controller output pressure, bellows 3 will contract, pulling actuating lever 1 to the left, thus uncovering nozzle 5. This bleeds air from relay bellows 8, seating the relay valve to vent air from the valve motor. The motor air pressure will decrease until the valve stem is sufficiently raised (or lowered, depending on the motor action) to rotate actuating lever 1, and, therefore, the flapper, back to a position adjacent to the nozzle. This positioner may be mounted on the motor top,

Information Sheet 8

as a sealed unit, resulting in complete protection to the linkage from moisture and corrosion. See Fig. 102.

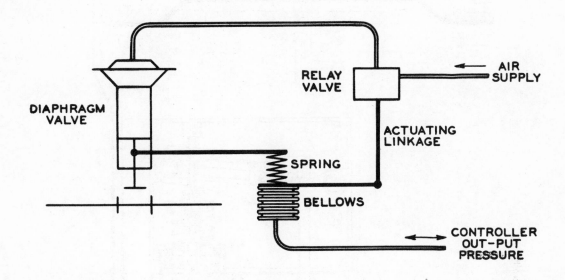

Fig. 116 - Schematic Diagram of a Valve Positioner

Fig. 116 is a schematic diagram of another type of valve positioner. In this positioner the force exerted by a bellows which is inflated with the controller output pressure is balanced against the force of a spring. One end of the spring is positioned by a linkage which is operated by the valve push-rod.

The relay valve is operated by means of a linkage which transmits the combined reactions of the bellows and spring. Hence, when the controller output pressure decreases, the pilot valve linkage is moved downward and air is released from the diaphragm chamber. The valve push-rod then moves upward and the spring tension lifts the relay valve actuating linkage until equilibrium is restored.

When the controller output pressure increases, the relay valve actuating linkage is moved upward and air is admitted to the diaphragm chamber moving the valve downward. The linkage is thus moved downward until equilibrium is again restored.

Schematic diagrams of the type shown in Figs. 112 and 116 are simplified and do not show the details of any positioner. Adjustments in the valve positioners which compensate for the different lengths of valve travel and for the various pressure ranges must be provided to insure satisfactory operation.

Information Sheet 8

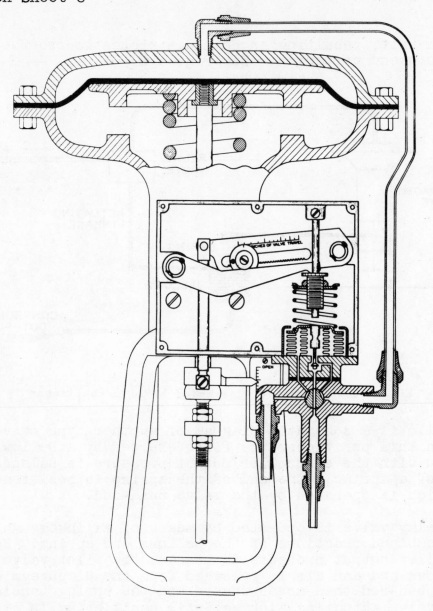

Fig. 117 - Valve Positioner and Diaphragm Motor
Courtesy of Moore Products Company

Fig. 117 shows the details of construction of a positioner of
the type shown in Fig. 116. Note that the valve travel adjuster
increases or decreases the effective leverage of the arm which is
actuated by the valve stem. Moving the adjuster to the right increases the amount of valve travel. Adjustment is also provided
for the regulation of the balance spring compression.

The pilot valve is a double seated valve which admits air to
the diaphragm valve when the pilot is seated against the upper seat

Information Sheet 8

but bleeds air to the atmosphere when it is in an intermediate position or cuts off the air supply when in contact with the lower seat.

If the controller air pressure is increased, expansion of the bellows will cause the pilot to be lifted. Air will then be admitted to the diaphragm causing a lowering of the valve stem, increasing the spring pressure against the bellows and lowering the pilot until a balance is reached between the controlled air pressure and the pressure of the balance spring caused by the position of the valve stem.

Information Sheet 9   INDUSTRIAL CONTROLLER APPLICATIONS

Many controller applications are used in industry to maintain conditions which are necessary to the manufacture of a quality product.

It is not within the scope of this monograph to describe all of the possible applications for any given industry. However, this unit and those immediately following give illustrations and descriptions of typical installations of controllers in the process industries.

Blancher Control

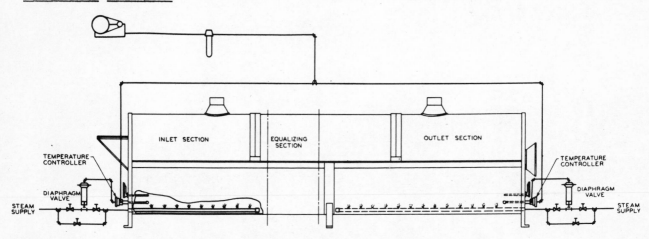

Fig. 118 - Temperature Controller of a Blancher
Courtesy of Taylor Instrument Companies

A blancher, Fig. 118, is a long cylindrical vessel through which vegetables are carried on a conveyor, and in which they are pre-cooked for a short period preparatory to canning. The blancher is heated by steam admitted through perforated pipes, directly into the water.

It is important in this process to control the temperature just at the boiling point to insure a quality product. Since the blancher has considerable heat capacity, it is easily controlled

DIAPHRAGM VALVE SYMBOLS

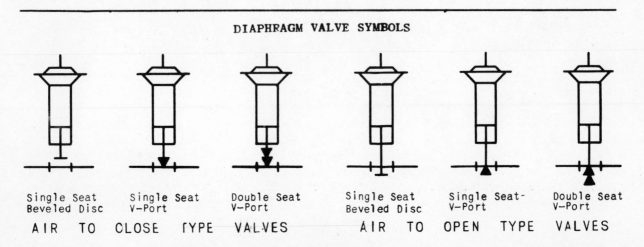

Single Seat Beveled Disc	Single Seat V-Port	Double Seat V-Port	Single Seat Beveled Disc	Single Seat V-Port	Double Seat V-Port
AIR TO CLOSE TYPE VALVES			AIR TO OPEN TYPE VALVES		

Information Sheet 9

by an air-operated, expansion stem controller with a relatively
high sensitivity. One controller is installed at the inlet end,
and another at the outlet, with the temperature sensitive bulbs
and industrial thermometers installed just above the steam inlet
pipes to cut down time lag. The controllers actuate diaphragm
valves in the steam supply lines of the respective sections.

Open Cooker Control

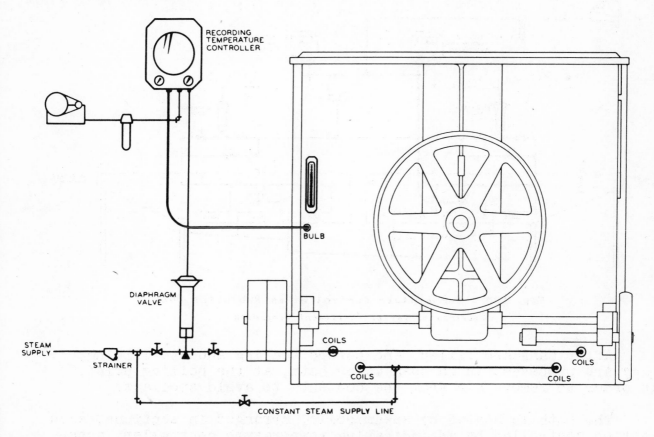

Fig. 119 - Temperature Control of an Open Cooker
Courtesy of Taylor Instrument Companies

        Open cookers in a canning plant may be either of the batch or
continuous type. In these, the cans of produce are sterilized at
the boiling point corresponding to atmospheric pressure. The bath
is heated by steam, entering coils near the bottom of the vessel,
under control of a recording temperature controller of the high
sensitivity or on-and-off type. This controller operates a diaphragm valve in the steam supply line. See Fig. 119. A constant
and insufficient amount of steam is supplied through a hand valve
to a bank of separate coils. The additional steam necessary for
proper control at the required temperature is admitted by the
controller and valve.

Information Sheet 9

    This application can be satisfied by a high sensitivity con-
troller because of the high heat capacity effect of the apparatus.
Circulation of the bath is adequate due to boiling, and on continuous cookers, the passage of the cans through the cookers provides
agitation.

Exhauster Box Control

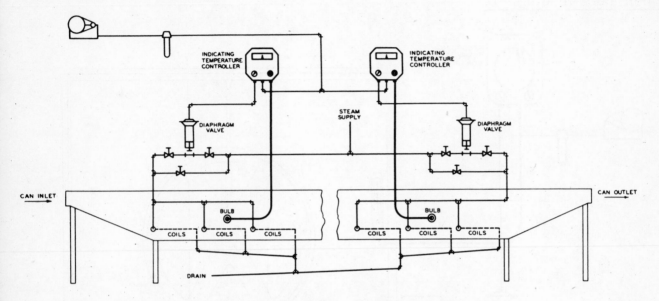

Fig. 120 - Temperature Control of an Exhauster Box
Courtesy of Taylor Instrument Companies

    After cans are filled, and before sealing and sterilizing,
they are processed in an open water bath, at the boiling point,
in order to remove air from the contents to avoid spoilage.

    The bath is heated by steam coils, arranged in sections, each
section controlled by an indicating temperature controller, actuating a diaphragm valve supplying steam to its bank of coils. See
Fig. 120.

    The bulbs of the temperature controllers are located just
above the coils, so as to reduce the time lag of the system. This
combined with adequate circulation provided by the passage of the
cans through the exhauster permits a high sensitivity controller
to be used.

    On applications of this type where the boiling point must be
maintained at atmospheric pressure, considerable savings of steam
are possible through the use of automatic control equipment, because only sufficient steam is admitted to produce boiling.

Information Sheet 9

Vertical Retort Control

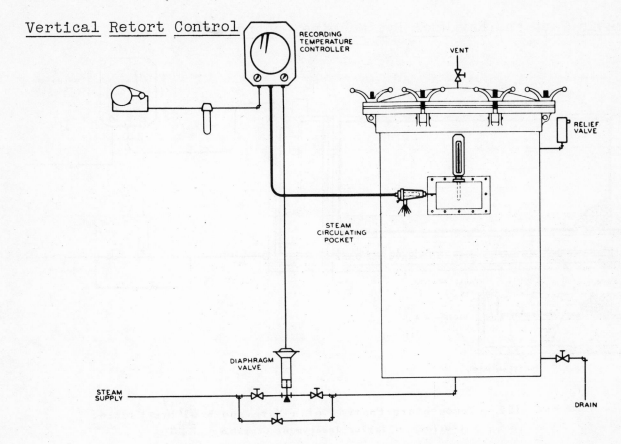

Fig. 121 - Temperature Control of a Vertical Retort
Courtesy of Taylor Instrument Companies

An example of a relatively simple but very critical batch process is the dry steam cooking or sterilization of canned products in a closed vessel, commonly called a retort, under pressure. The retort is packed with cans placed in large baskets. Each can must be heated; those at the bottom the same as those at the top. Consequently, all air must be vented at the beginning of the cook.

The bulb of the temperature controller is placed in a fitting outside the retort, and steam from the retort is allowed to escape through the fitting, thus providing good circulation by the bulb. See Fig. 121. Steam enters the retort through a ring of perforated pipes at the bottom of the retort, controlled by a diaphragm valve under control of a recording temperature controller.

The controller must operate in very high sensitivity as the retort must be brought to cooking temperature as quickly as possible and without overpeaking, and then accurately held at that temperature. The time lag of this application is short, and in order to utilize the advantage of high sensitivity to obtain the results required, it is essential to use a diaphragm motor of minimum volume and a short air line from controller to valve.

Information Sheet 9

Skein Yarn and Raw Wool Dye Machine Control

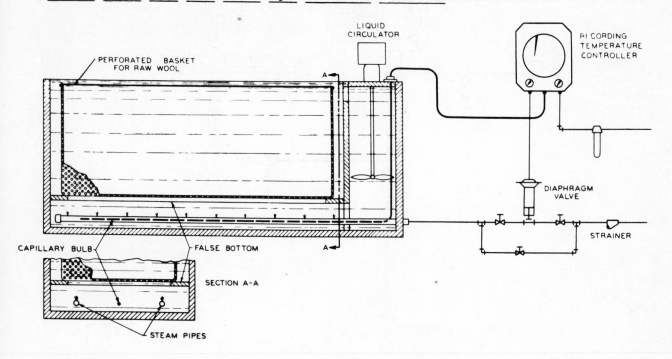

Fig. 122 - Temperature Control of a Yarn and Wool Dye Machine
Courtesy of Taylor Instrument Companies

Fig. 122 shows the application of a proportional response recording controller to a skein yarn and raw wool dye machine. In
operation, the skeins are suspended on a rack which is lowered into
the machine by a chain fall. In the case of raw wool, the material
is placed in a perforated basket which in turn sits on a false bottom. The dye liquor is circulated through the mass alternately in
one direction and then the other, to obtain a quick and uniform
penetration.

In the past, the conventional method of applying controllers
was to use a regular type of bulb placed in the vertical section in
which the reversible motor-operated propeller is located. This type
of installation possessed the shortcoming in that when the circulation is downward, the bulb is in a position where it is subjected
to a detrimental amount of time lag.

Two things have been done to improve the installation. First,
the use of a capillary type bulb; second, installing it between
the perforated steam pipes in such a way that very little time lag
exists regardless of the direction of the circulation. The new
bulb location makes it possible to use a higher controller sensitivity than has been practical in the past. This in turn results
in less drift in the control point, the advantages of which are
better protection against boiling over when operating at 210°

Information Sheet 9

which is usually the case, and quicker rise to the holding temperature. Sensitivity settings are about 75 psi per inch.

In the case of the raw wool dye machine, very frequently a
Time Schedule Controller is used instead of the proportional response recording controller. The nature of the material requires
different dye stuffs than in the case of yarn, and also a more
closely controlled temperature with respect to time. The capillary
bulb in the new position is equally advantageous on this installation.

Milk Pasteurizer Control

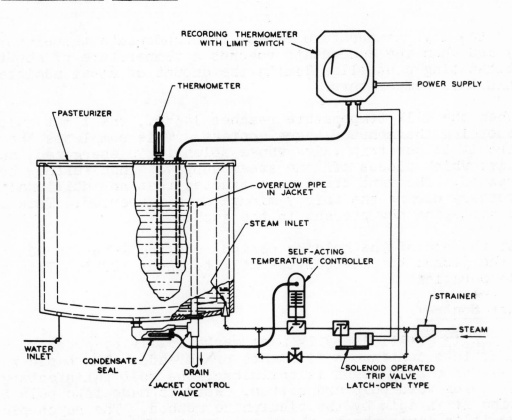

Fig. 123 - Temperature Control of a Milk Pasteurizer
Courtesy of Taylor Instrument Companies

This is a batch process where the control instruments act as
limit controllers. Milk is pumped into the vat equipped with a
steam jacket and must be heated to 143°F. and held at that temperature for thirty minutes. See Fig. 123. It must be heated as rapidly
as possible to prevent bacteria growth and not allowed to be heated
excessively over 143°F., as the quality and flavor of the milk are
impaired.

At the start of the heating period, the milk temperature is low.
The recording thermometer is equipped with a limit switch actuated
by the Bourdon spring which also records the temperature of the

milk. The limit switch circuit is open, and the solenoid-operated trip valve is de-energized.

To start, the trip valve in the steam inlet line is latched open, manually. This turns the steam on, and it passes through the valve of the self-acting temperature controller to the jacket. The steam condenses in the jacket on the walls of the lining, and in so doing, gives up heat to the milk which is being agitated continuously during the process. The bulb of the self-acting controller is placed in a condensate seal in the jacket outlet. At the beginning, the condensate is cool, calling for a wide open steam valve.

As the milk temperature rises, the condensate temperature also rises, and when the condensate reaches a temperature of about $160^{\circ}F$. the self-acting controller limits the amount of steam admitted to maintain this temperature.

When the milk temperature reaches $143^{\circ}F$., the limit switch in the recording thermometer makes contact. This completes the electrical circuit to the trip valve whose solenoid is energized, and trips the valve which closes off the steam supply. Thus further heating is arrested. The vats are so constructed that no additional heat is necessary during the thirty minute holding period. This is due to the air space now present in the jacket.

At the end of the holding period, cooling water is admitted to flood the jacket to pre-cool the milk to about $100^{\circ}F$. This is a manual operation.

Shredder Control

Rayon is artificial silk made mechanically by pressing a viscous mass into continuous filaments or threads. The basic raw material for making rayon is cellulose, the most satisfactory source of this being wood pulp and cotton. Wood is made into pulp by digesting it in acid by the bisulphite method. The rayon plants receive it in large sheets which are first steeped in caustic, and then squeezed to remove the excess caustic.

The next operation is breaking up the sheets in a shredder, a machine containing a pair of rotating blades, Fig. 124. The bottom of the shredder forms two half cylinders, at the junction of which is a serrated saddle. The teeth of the blades passing across the teeth of the saddle shred the cellulose into fluffly, snow-white crumbs. This results in an exothermic reaction and makes necessary a cooling jacket to carry off the heat generated. Brine or cooled water is used as the cooling medium.

The sheets are dropped into the shredder when charging, and sometimes large bundles of these are dropped at once. This action

Information Sheet 9

and that of the revolving blades whipping the large sheets about causes severe strains on any thermometer bulb installed in the machine.

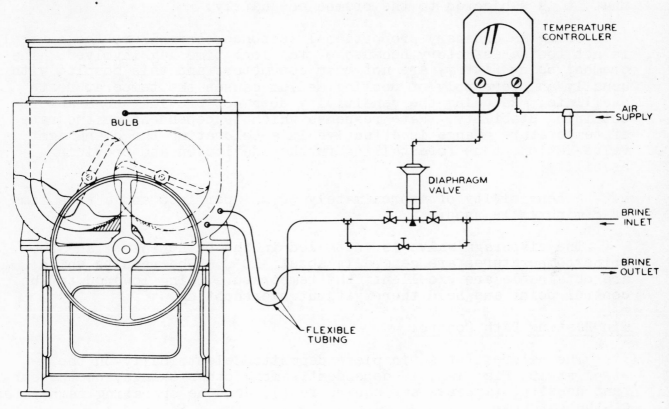

Fig. 124 - Temperature Control of a Shredder
Courtesy of Taylor Instrument Companies

The shredding operation takes from 2 to 3 hours and the rotation of the blades is reversed at regular intervals. Shredding takes place when the blades rotate in the forward direction and when running in reverse, a mixing action takes place. Shredding not only thoroughly mixes the sodium cellulose but assists in the aging which is the next phase of the rayon process. The temperature maintained in the shredder has a profound effect on the aging and because of this, temperature control is very essential to efficient operation.

In the shredder controller, the bulb is generally of heavy construction to withstand the abuse of the sheets. A short overall chart range is desirable and this means a large bulb volume. As a result, a long tubular type bulb is usually employed, extending entirely across the shredder, and securely anchored at both ends. This construction also results in an average temperature indication, and relatively quick response due to the large bulb surface.

Information Sheet 9

Bulb construction is not the only answer to good control, but location is also a factor. It is placed slightly out of line of the weight of the pulp as it is dumped into the shredder, but so that it is subjected to the crumbs adequately.

Using an ordinary proportional response controller, the control is not too satisfactory because of the long time lag involved. The crumbs, being fluffy, are not good conductors and this coupled with usually an oversupply of cooling medium causes the temperature to oscillate. Reducing the sensitivity does not provide the means for obtaining stability. Rate response which is dependent on the rate of temperature change is effective in accelerating the diaphragm valve action, thus forestalling further deviation and providing stability.

A sensitivity of approximately 50 psi per inch and a rate time of 8 minutes is used.

The diaphragm valve is installed in the brine inlet, and the brine temperatures are generally about $-10^{\circ}C$. The results which are obtainable are excellent, the temperature being lowered to the control point and held there without overshooting.

Tin Plating Bath Control

The nature of the tin plate deposited electrically on the steel strip, Fig. 125, is dependent, among other things, on the current density, (amperes per square foot), and the operating temperature of the bath.

The plating speed is directly proportional to the current density. The power required to deposit a given quantity of tin is inversely proportional to the conductivity of the electrolyte. The reason for an increase in the temperature of the plating solution is to increase its conductivity and thus provide more rapid plating and a more economical use of current. As the result of current passing through the electrolyte, heat is generated internally.

The bath temperature, if not arrested, will rise until it is high enough to dissipate the heat as rapidly as it is generated. In some cases, this temperature may be higher than the desired or efficient operating temperature. It is then necessary to provide some means of cooling the solution. Other baths having higher points of maximum efficiency may require heating.

Fig. 125 shows the equipment used for automatic control of the plating bath temperature, utilizing both heating and cooling. The indicating temperature controller has its temperature sensitive bulb located in the heat exchanger outlet line. A separable well is used so that the bulb will not be attacked by the corrosive

Information Sheet 9

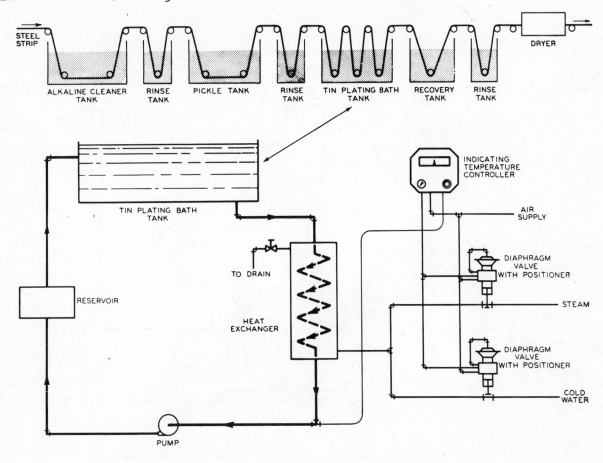

Fig. 125 - Temperature Control for a Tin Plating Bath
Courtesy of Taylor Instrument Companies

action of the plating solution. A lead sheathed well is recommended.

The controller action is such that an increase in temperature at the bulb causes a decrease in the controller output air pressure. This pressure decrease tends to close the steam valve and open the water valve, thus correcting for temperature change.

When starting the process, the solution in the plating tank is cold, the controller output air pressure is at a maximum, the cooling water valve is closed, the steam valve is open, and the solution heats up rapidly until the operating temperature is reached.

To prevent the simultaneous admission of steam and cooling water, the operating sensitivities of the valve positioners are such that the steam valve starts to close at 18 psi and is completely closed at 10 psi. The water valve starts to open at 10 psi and is fully opened at 2 psi. When the temperature rises above the control point, due to heat generated by the flow of current and the internal resistance of the plating solution, the controller output pressure falls below 10 psi, thus admitting cooling water to the heat exchanger.

Information Sheet 9

Pulp Grinder Control

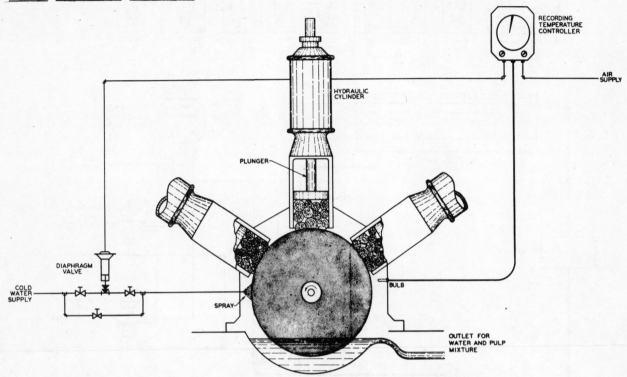

RECORDING
TEMPERATURE
CONTROLLER

AIR
SUPPLY

HYDRAULIC
CYLINDER

PLUNGER

DIAPHRAGM
VALVE

COLD
WATER
SUPPLY

SPRAY

BULB

OUTLET FOR
WATER AND PULP
MIXTURE

Fig. 126 - Temperature Control of a Pulp Grinder
Courtesy of Taylor Instrument Companies

A rather unique temperature control application is found in the process of wood pulp preparation by means of grinding. In this application the debarked logs are placed in pockets as shown in Fig. 126, and by means of a hydraulic pressure, the logs are held against a revolving stone and the wood is pulped by its grinding action.

Since the grinding operation produces heat, this must be removed by applying cooling water to the stone. This cooling water mixes with the pulp to provide a means for handling the pulp and the amount of water used determines the consistency of the pulp. It is recognized in the paper industry that uniform temperature is an important phase in efficient grinder operation.

The bulb of the temperature controller is located in such a position that the splash of the pulp and water from the stone or grinder pit will reach the bulb so that it can record the pit temperature. The controller actuates a diaphragm valve installed in a water supply line to the shower, in order to obtain satisfactory temperature in the pit. The diaphragm valve is usually supplied with some adjustment by which the valve can never completely close

Information Sheet 9

off. This is a safety measure as the stone must be protected from excessive temperatures which would cause it to blister and crack.

The bulb used is generally of a length to reach completely across the stone's surface in order to obtain a sensitive type bulb. The operating sensitivity of the pulp grinder temperature controller is approximately 20 psi per inch. Automatic temperature control of a pulp grinder usually results in a higher rate of production for a given stock quality, lower power consumption, improved and more constant quality of stock, as shown by the freeness, a more constant consistency of the stock and a lower stone cost due to a longer stone life, which is enhanced by fewer burring operations, less flaking of the stone at the surface because extreme temperature changes are eliminated, and elimination of the possibility of stone fracture caused by sudden temperature changes.

Information Sheet 10   SPECIALIZED FORMS OF CONTROLLERS

Using the basic fundamentals of an automatic controller design, several modifications are possible which permit the field of automatic control to be broadened. Such modifications for specialized form controllers include remote pneumatic transmission systems, ratio controllers, pneumatic set controllers, and time schedule controllers. All of these are applicable to controllers of temperature, pressure, humidity, rate of flow, and liquid level.

A brief description of each of the above mentioned four 'cousins' of the automatic controller follows. These are descriptions of the Taylor design, although instruments of other manufacturers are quite similar in effect, and accomplish, fundamentally, the same purpose.

A. Remote Pneumatic Transmission Systems

Remote Pneumatic Transmission Systems provide a simple, accurate, and in many instances the only practical and economical means of indicating, recording or controlling process variables remote from the point of measurement. Remote transmission is particularly advantageous in oil refineries, chemical plants, air conditioning work, or in any plant where it is desirable to correlate temperature, pressure, flow or liquid level data, on a centralized panel, or in a control room.

Transmitters utilize fundamentally standard instruments. The system may consist of one or two transmitters, connected to a receiver by small diameter copper tubing, using air pressure as the transmitting medium. Or there may be one or more receiving instruments, not necessarily near each other, and they may be as far as 1000 feet from the transmitter. Transmitters or receivers may be indicating, recording or controlling

When a transmission system is properly installed, the accuracy is well within plus or minus 1% of the scale range. This high degree of accuracy is particularly important where the receiver is also the controller. The speed of response of the receiver to changes in output air pressure from the transmitter is largely dependent upon the length of the connecting tubing. For rough calculation purposes, the maximum lag may be assumed to be one second per hundred feet of connecting tubing, although it rarely is as great as this.

Remote pneumatic transmission does away with the dangers of electrical circuits in explosive atmospheres. It measures, transmits and receives continuously, regardless of electric current failures. Should the connecting tubing between transmitter and receiver be damaged it can be quickly and inexpensively replaced.

The use of pneumatic transmission extends all the desirable performance characteristics of air operated control. Furthermore, a receiving instrument is a universal instrument and may be used for pressure, flow, or liquid level by merely changing the chart or scale,

Information Sheet 10

because all receivers operate on the same pressure range.

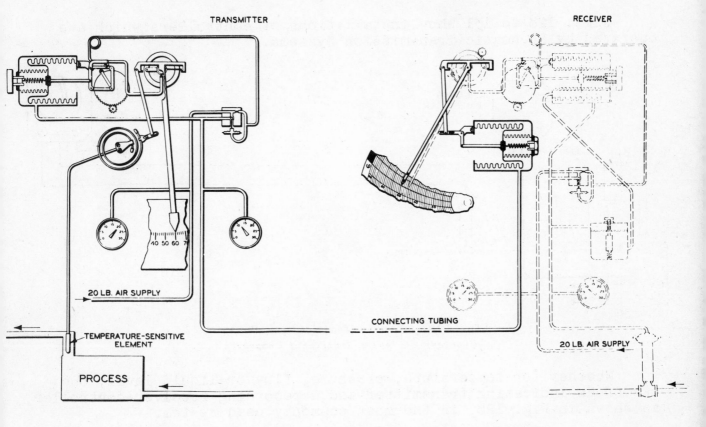

TRANSMITTER   RECEIVER

20 LB. AIR SUPPLY

TEMPERATURE-SENSITIVE ELEMENT

PROCESS

CONNECTING TUBING

20 LB. AIR SUPPLY

Fig. 127 - Schematic Diagram of a Remote Pneumatic
Transmission System
Courtesy of Taylor Instrument Companies

Fig. 127 is a schematic diagram of a Remote Pneumatic Transmission System. The instrument at the left is known as the transmitter and the one at the right as the receiver.

Assume a temperature rise in the process at the lower left of the figure. The resulting motion of the baffle in the transmitter will vary the output pressure to the bellows shown in heavy lines in the receiver. This bellows will then adjust the pointer, or pen, of the receiver, causing its reading to correspond with that of the transmitter.

The receiver may also be a controller, as indicated by the broken lines. In this case its output pressure would be varied by the movement of its pointer and baffle and the corrective valve action would then be applied.

Besides correlating processing data in the control room or on a central panel, pneumatic transmission provides the operator out on the unit with an indicating or recording instrument for observation and eliminates the necessity of returning to the main control room in order to check the performance of the unit.

Information Sheet 10

1. Applications

Figs. 128 to 131 show installations of controllers which are operated by Pneumatic Transmission Systems.

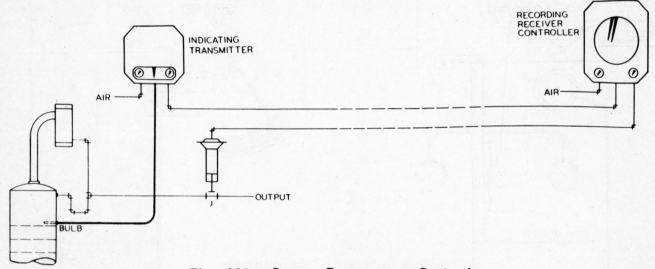

Fig. 128 - Remote Temperature Control
Courtesy of Taylor Instrument Companies

Whether for temperature, pressure, flow or liquid level, the use of an indicating transmitter and a recording receiver-controller, as shown in Fig. 128, is the most commonly used system.

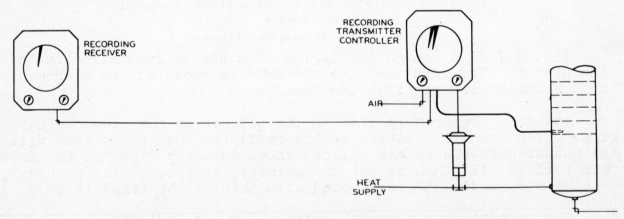

Fig. 129 - Remote Record of Controlled Temperature
Courtesy of Taylor Instrument Companies

The hook-up shown in Fig. 129 provides for a recording transmitter-controller and a recording, non-controlling receiver.

Information Sheet 10

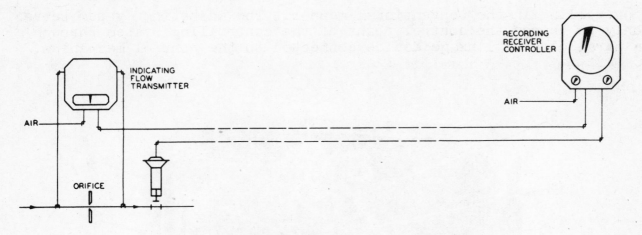

Fig. 130 - Remote Flow Control
Courtesy of Taylor Instrument Companies

Referring to Fig. 130, the flow rate is set at the receiver controller while the transmitter is adjacent to the orifice. Automatic reset permits throttling control and constant flow in spite of load changes.

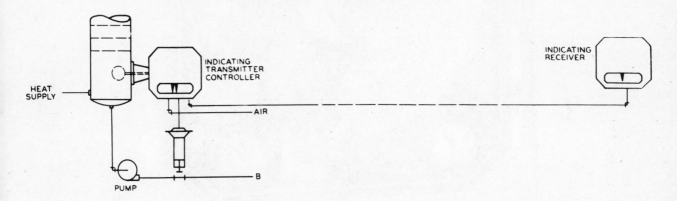

Fig. 131 - Remote Liquid Level Indication
Courtesy of Taylor Instrument Companies

Both the transmitting and the receiving instruments shown in Fig. 131 are of the indicating type which furnish no record.

B. Ratio Controller

The Ratio Controller is an instrument in which changes in one variable adjust the control point of another variable. The controlling and adjusting systems are separate, each with its own functions, and yet interlocked in such a manner as to produce the desired predetermined results. The controlling system does the actual

Information Sheet 10

controlling in the conventional manner. The adjusting system serves only to change the control point of the controlling system through a parallelogram linkage device connected to the control mechanism.

Fig. 132 - Recording Ratio Controller
Courtesy of Taylor Instrument Companies

Illustrated in Fig. 132 is a cutaway view of a Ratio Pressure Controller with adjustable sensitivity and automatic reset. Located in the right-hand side of the instrument case is the controlling system. Control is obtained from the motion of low pressure unit 4 which results from changes of the variable under control, and to which the instrument is connected. This motion is transmitted through connecting link 2, to pen arm 5, and also to the baffle lever. The action of the control mechanism is exactly the same as in the stand-ard Taylor Controller, whereby the nozzle and baffle arrangement produces air pressure variations through a relay air valve to a dia-phragm valve motor.

Information Sheet 10

Located in the left-hand side of the instrument case is the adjusting system. Automatic adjusting of the control point is effected
from the motion of the actuating element resulting from changes in
an uncontrolled apparatus to which bellows unit 6 is connected. Its
motion is transmitted through connecting link 3, to pen arm 7, and
to parallelogram 9, which actuates the baffle lever according to a
predetermined ratio setting. The differential between adjusting pen
and control pen may be set by knob 1.

Parallelogram 9, which is used to obtain ratio settings, is a
linkage device similar to that used in the adjustable sensitivity
unit of the standard Taylor Controller. The mechanism consists of
several links through which the motion of adjusting pen arm lever 3
actuates one end of the baffle lever. Ratio adjustments are made
with the aid of ratio dial 8 calibrated from three direct ratio to
zero to three inverse ratio. This will be explained in more detail
in the paragraphs which follow.

1. Terminology

    a. Adjusting system is that system which, actuated by the
       temperature, pressure, liquid level, or flow of the
       uncontrolled medium, resets the control point of the
       controlling system.

    b. Controlling system is that system which controls the
       temperature, pressure, liquid level, or flow and is
       set by the adjusting system.

    c. The term ratio indicates the amount of control point
       adjustment caused by a unit change in the uncontrolled
       pen such that:

       (1) A movement of one increment produced on the chart
           by the adjusting mechanism will cause a movement
           of three increments to be produced on the chart
           by the controlling mechanism set at 3 on the dial
           as one extreme, or such that:

       (2) A movement of the full width of the chart produced
           by the adjusting mechanism will cause no movement
           to be produced on the chart by the control mechan-
           ism set at zero on the dial as the other extreme.

       (3) Intermediate settings are, of course, available as
           outlined above.

    d. The term direct ratio indicates that for an increase in
       the temperature, pressure, liquid level, or flow of the
       uncontrolled medium, an increase in the temperature,

Information Sheet 10

pressure, flow, or liquid level of the controlled medium
will be effected. Thus, an outward movement of the
adjusting pen will result in an outward movement of the
control pen.

e. The term inverse ratio indicates that for an increase
in the temperature, pressure, liquid level, or flow of
the uncontrolled medium, a decrease in temperature, pressure, liquid level, or flow of the controlled medium will
be effected. Thus, an outward movement of the adjusting
pen will result in an inward movement of the control pen.

f. Differential is the difference between the related conditions in the apparatus, as indicated at any one time by
the position of the adjusting and control pens.

g. Operating Range of the adjusting system is that range
through which the adjusting pen is expected to have effect
on the control pen.

2. Ratio Adjustment

On Ratio Controllers, the amount the control pen will be repo-
sitioned by the adjusting pen is determined by the setting of ratio
dial 8. The relationship at various direct and inverse ratio settings is shown in Fig. 133 a and b. The coordinates of the curves
are in per cent of the chart range. A mastery of this type of chart
will be of considerable aid in visualizing the action of ratio controllers.

With the differential adjusted so that the two pens have a common zero at the inner circle of the recorder chart, as indicated by
the graph, Fig. 133a, the control pen will be adjusted directly in
accordance with the ratio setting. For example, if the ratio is
0.8 when the adjusting pen has traveled over 50% of the chart range,
the control pen will travel 40% of the chart range. When the adjusting pen is at 100%, the control pen is at 80%. If the adjusting
ratio is 1, the two pens are always together.

Fig. 133b illustrates the adjusting ratio curves for inverse
ratios. The differential is adjusted so that when the adjusting pen
is at 100% of its travel, the controlling pen is at zero. The control
pen will be adjusted in accordance with the inverse ratio setting.
For example, if the ratio is at 0.5 when the adjusting pen is at 40%,
the control pen is at 30%. When the adjusting pen is at 0, the
control pen is at 50%.

Information Sheet 10

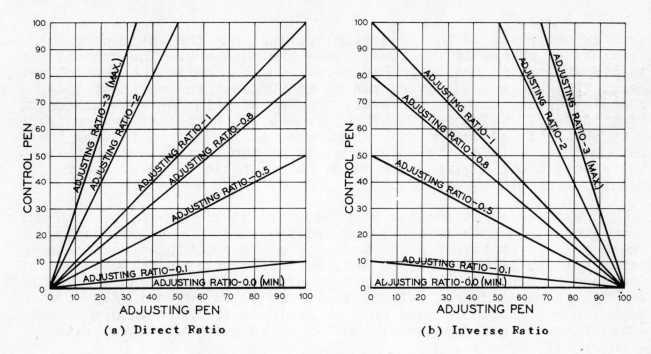

(a) Direct Ratio   (b) Inverse Ratio

Fig. 133 - Adjusting Ratio Curves
Courtesy of Taylor Instrument Companies

Fig. 134 illustrates the effect of turning knob 1, with the ratio dial set at 0.8 direct. The slope of the curves is always the same. The relationship between the coordinates is not the

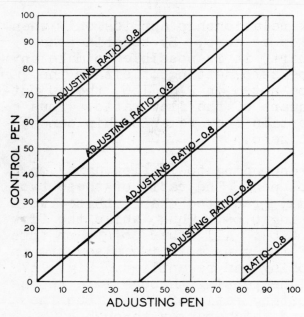

Fig. 134 - Direct Ratio

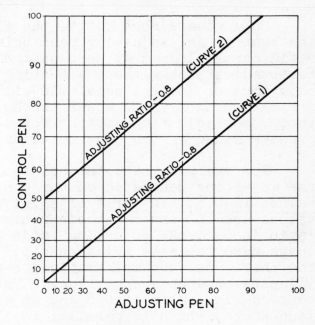

Fig. 135 - Direct Ratio

Adjusting Ratio Curves
Courtesy of Taylor Instrument Companies

Information Sheet 10

same as the ratio of the adjusting setting; but the ratio of the increments of change is the same. Take the case where the control pen
is 30% and the adjusting pen is zero. On this curve the control pen
reads 70% when the adjusting pen is at 50%, but the ratio of the
coordinates is not 0.8. However, the increase in the control pen is
from 30 to 70, which is 40. The increase in the adjusting pen is from
0 to 50. This adjustment is useful when it is desired to vary the
zero point of either the adjusting pen or the control pen so that the
increments above a given zero value have a ratio of .8 of the full
value of the other variable.

Now these relationships work out very nicely on charts with uniform scales, such as mercury, gas and pressure. On vapor charts,
which are not uniformly graduated, the basic principles remain the
same, but the results must be analyzed differently. The movement of
the pens is linear, but the corresponding temperature changes are not,
due to the non-linearity of the charts as illustrated in Fig. 135.
Vapor charts should be used only on Ratio Controllers when the operating range of both systems is small, or when in 1.0 direct ratio
with no differential.

With a Ratio Controller in which flow adjusts flow and one flow
is small compared to the other, the orifices should be proportioned
so that each will cause its pen to cover the major portion of the
chart. Instead of using the same size orifice in both lines, the
one having the lower flow should employ a smaller orifice.

On a square root chart, the flow relationship applies only when
the control and adjusting pens coincide at zero. By squaring the
ratio parallelogram at zero on the chart, it is possible to make any
ratio adjustment without affecting the zero setting of either the
adjusting or control pens. As will be noted in Fig. 136, the adjusting ratio has a value equal to the square of the flow ratio. Thus
the proper adjusting setting for a certain flow relationship can be
predetermined if the pens coincide at zero.

For example, take the point corresponding to 10 flow units on
the adjusting pen and 8 on the control pen. The ratio of these two
values is 0.8. In terms of a uniformly graduated chart, these two
values are 100 and 64, their ratio being 0.64. Thus, while the flow
ratio is 0.8, the adjusting ratio is 0.64. All other points on this
curve have the same relationship. If the pens coincide elsewhere on
the chart, no such mathematical reasoning can be applied. Fig. 137
illustrates such a condition. The line passing through zero represents a flow ratio of 0.8 and an adjusting ratio of 0.64. But the
line above, which is parallel to it and which passes through 4.2
cannot be said to have a definite flow ratio. Each point on this
line has a different flow ratio from all other points on it.

Information Sheet 10

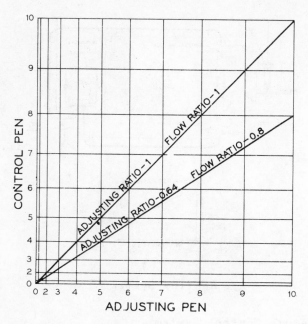

Fig. 136 - Direct Ratio

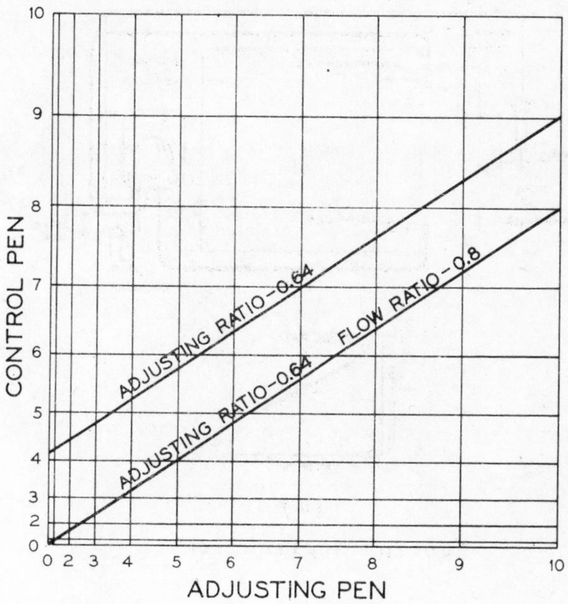

Fig. 137 - Direct Ratio

Adjusting Ratio Curves

Courtesy of Taylor Instrument Companies

3. Applications

For air conditioning large rooms, it is often desirable to reduce the temperature of the incoming air from the conditioner, as
the temperature of the return air increases, as in the summer.
Return air temperature increases are due either to body heat or
changes in outdoor conditions. As soon as the uncontrollable factors, such as body heat, and the effects of outside conditions come
into play, the temperature of the incoming air will then be too warm
to provide comfortable conditions. It becomes essential, therefore,
to change the temperature of the incoming air in relation to change
in temperature of the outgoing air. To do this automatically is
precisely the purpose of the Ratio Controller.

Fig. 138a illustrates schematically this type of application.
The controlling bulb of the instrument is located in the air duct
from the conditioner, and the adjusting bulb is located in return
air duct to the conditioner. As the return air temperature changes,
the adjusting system automatically resets the incoming air temperature in some predetermined inverse ratio relationship, as illustrated
by the curve in Fig. 138a.

Another application in this same field is the varying of room
temperature in accordance with outside air temperature changes.
Especially in the winter, as the outdoor temperature drops, it is
desirable to raise the room temperature. Here again, the Ratio
Controller is the instrument to automatically produce the necessary
room control point changes according to temperature changes at the

Information Sheet 10

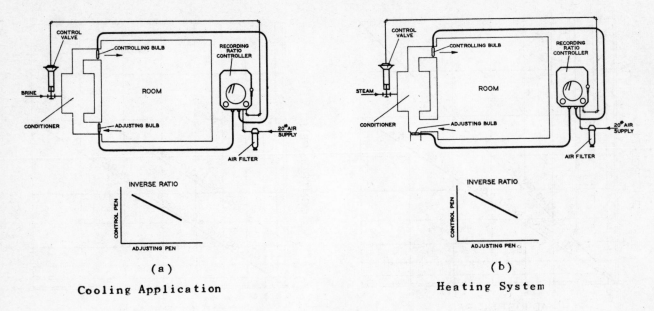

Fig. 138 - Patio Temperature Control System
Courtesy of Taylor Instrument Companies

adjusting bulb which is located in the inlet air duct to the conditioner. Such an application illustrates also that the action of the
adjusting bulb is anticipatory, since the inside temperature will
be caused to change in advance of the normal response of the controlling bulb, as the latter would be actuated solely by air infil-
tration. Illustrated in Fig. 138b is a typical application. The
controlling bulb of the instrument is located in the air duct from
the conditioner, and the adjusting bulb is exposed to the outside
air in the inlet air duct. As the outside air temperature changes,
the inlet air temperature will also change accordingly, since the
controller is set in inverse ratio, as indicated by the chart in
Fig. 138b.

Information Sheet 10

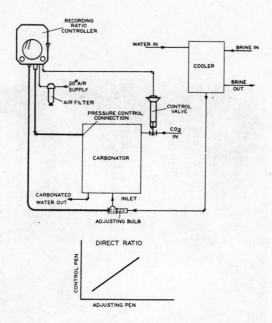

Fig. 139 - Beverage Carbonation Control
Courtesy of Taylor Instrument Companies

In the manufacture of carbonated beverages, the carbonation process is extremely important to the quality of the product. Each variety of beverage bottled has a very definite amount of carbon dioxide by volume which must be dissolved in the liquid ingredients. To assure that the correct volume of gas is dissolved in the beverages, is the function of a Ratio Controller. This application is illustrated schematically in Fig. 139. The bulb of the adjusting system is located in the water line from the cooler. The controlling system is connected to the carbonator. Thus a change in water temperature adjusts the pressure of carbon dioxide in the carbonator. There is a very definite temperature-pressure relationship for the carbonation of water, since it is a proven fact that water of a given temperature will absorb just so much carbon dioxide gas at a given pressure.

C. Pneumatic Set Controller

Increasing complexities in modern processing constantly produce problems in which a temperature, pressure, flow, or liquid level must automatically conform to changes in another variable related to the same process. As a result, the Pneumatic Set Controller, Fig. 140, was developed. It is fundamentally a standard controller with an added pneumatic adjustment, unit 2. This unit converts changes in input air pressure into linear movements of set pointer 1. The magnitude of the linear set pointer movement per pound change in input air pressure is governed by the setting of adjustment dial 3. The unit also provides for set pointer adjustments to be made in either direction for an increase in input air pressure, and for

Information Sheet 10

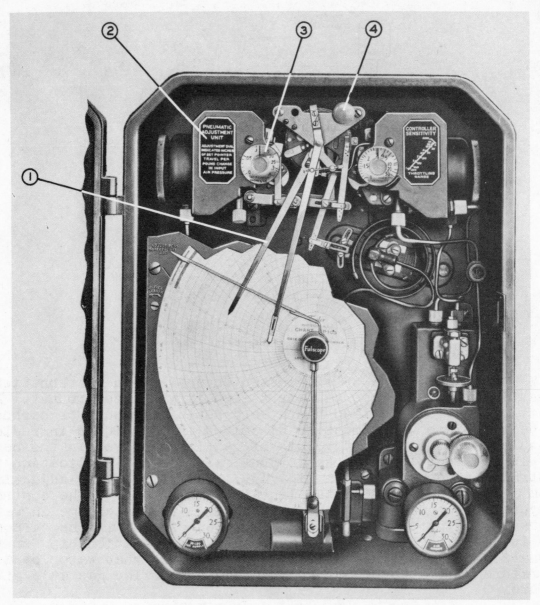

Fig. 140 - Cut-Away View of a Pneumatic Set Controller
Courtesy of Taylor Instrument Companies

limiting the travel of the set pointer within given limits. Also, the set pointer can be manually adjusted independently of the pneumatic set feature by use of knob 4.

The process variable used to adjust the controlled variable as controlled by the pneumatic set instrument may be controlled or uncontrolled, depending upon the particular application. However, regardless of whether the process variable is controlled or not, some means must be provided to detect the changes in this variable, and convert them into linear air pressure changes. Usually this is accomplished by a controller which hereafter will be referred

Information Sheet 10

to as the master controller or instrument. The output air pressure
from the master controller is transmitted to the pneumatic set controller to produce the required set pointer adjustment.

   The master instrument should be considered further in that it
may appear in several forms, entirely dependent upon the particular
application. In some cases it may be in the form of a transmitter,
while in others, as a conventional proportional response controller;
and in still others, as a proportional plus reset or proportional
plus rate response controller.

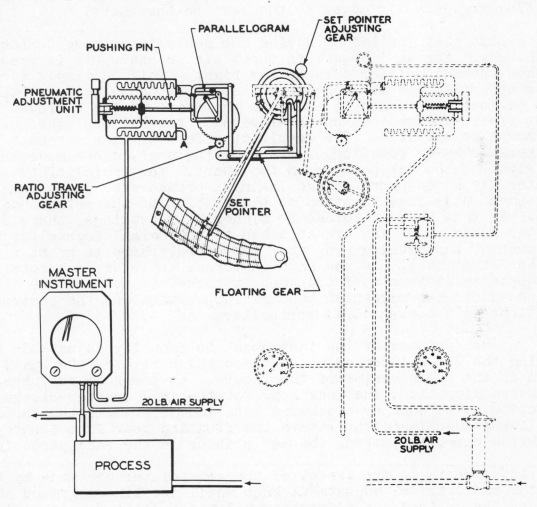

Fig. 141 - Schematic Diagram of a Pneumatic Set Control System
Courtesy of Taylor Instrument Companies

   Fig. 141 is a schematic view of a pneumatic set control system.
The units which provide for the pneumatic adjustment of the set
pointer are indicated in solid lines. Only the operation of the
pneumatic set feature will be discussed here. For information regarding the operation of the conventional control mechanism, see Information
Sheets 6 and 7.

Information Sheet 10

    Assume that the master instrument is a transmitter. Therefore, as the output pressure from the master transmitter increases from 3 to 18 psi, the set pointer of the Pneumatic Set Controller is linearly adjusted to the left on the chart. This is true since the output pressure is transmitted to the outside bellows connection of the pneumatic adjustment unit shown at the upper left of the figure. As the pressure increases on the outside of the bellows, the pushing pin moves to the right. The parallelogram transmits this motion to an arm and linkage which operates to move the floating gear in a clockwise direction. Since the set pointer is fastened to the face of the floating gear, it moves to the left on the chart.

    Assume that instead of having the set pointer move to the left on the chart for an increase in input air pressure, it is required to have the set pointer move to the right. This is simply accomplished by transferring the air tube from its present connection to the inside bellows connection A, shown to the right of the bellows. As the input pressure increases on the inside of the bellows, the pushing pin moves to the left. The resultant effect of this movement is a counter-clockwise rotation of the floating gear, and a movement to the right of the set pointer on the chart. The travel of the set pointer for a one-pound change in input pressure to the pneumatic adjustment unit is a function of the setting of the set pointer travel knob. As this knob is turned to higher dial settings, there is greater movement of the arm attached to the parallelogram for a given movement of the pushing pin, and, therefore, there is greater travel of the set pointer. As the knob is turned to lower dial settings, the opposite is true. If the knob is turned to zero on the dial, the pneumatic set mechanism becomes inoperative and the instrument functions as a conventional controller.

    The set pointer of the instrument is manually adjustable by turning the set pointer adjusting knob which rotates the small gear shown in the upper center of the figure. As the knob is turned in a clockwise direction, the back gear rotates in a counter-clockwise direction. The counter-clockwise rotation is transmitted through the linkage causing it to rotate the floating gear in a counter-clockwise direction, moving the set pointer in the same direction.

    Adjustments in the travel of the set pointer are made by turning the ratio travel adjustment knob until the line engraved thereon is over the desired set pointer travel, as indicated on the dial underneath. The dial is calibrated in inches of set pointer movement per pound change in output air pressure from the master instrument. The units range from 0 to .4 per pound; actually, however, it is possible to obtain values slightly in excess of .4 inches per pound by turning the knob beyond this point. To determine the dial setting which will produce the required set pointer travel for a given change in air pressure from the master instrument, use the following simple equation:

Information Sheet 10

$$\frac{A}{B} = C$$

Where: A = linear distance of set pointer travel in
           inches measured on a line drawn radially
           from the center of the chart.
       B = total change in output air pressure from
           master instrument.
       C = ratio travel dial setting in inches per pound.

Example: Assume that it is required to move the set pointer
3 inches on the chart when the output air pressure from the master
instrument varies from 2 to 17 psi.

$$\frac{A}{B} = C, \qquad \frac{3}{17-2} = \frac{3}{15} = .2 = \text{dial setting}$$

When the knob is turned to zero on the dial, there is no adjustment of the set pointer. When this occurs, the Pneumatic Set
Controller functions as a conventional controller. Its operation is
comparable to that of a controller set to high sensitivity where no
follow-up motion of the nozzle occurs.

1. Applications

The clearest way to present the utility of the Pneumatic Set
Controller is to cite several typical applications of this instrument. The following applications show that the Pneumatic Set Controller is very useful in solving many difficult control problems.

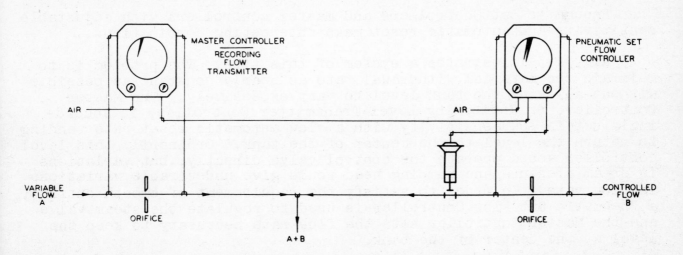

Fig. 142 - Flow Controlling Pneumatic Set
Courtesy of Taylor Instrument Companies

Fig. 142 shows an application involving a Pneumatic Set Flow
Controller and a Recording Flow Transmitter. The problem presented

Information Sheet 10

here is one of blending two fluids, A and B in correct proportion by volume. Flow A is variable; therefore, as it increases controlled flow B must be increased proportionately to maintain the correct blend. The Recording Flow Transmitter is connected in variable flow line A, and its transmitted output air pressure adjusts the set pointer of the Pneumatic Set Flow Controller. The control mechanism in the Pneumatic Set Controller is actuated by controlled flow B. The Pneumatic Set Controller automatically regulates controlled flow B according to some predetermined relationship, to correspond to changes in variable flow A.

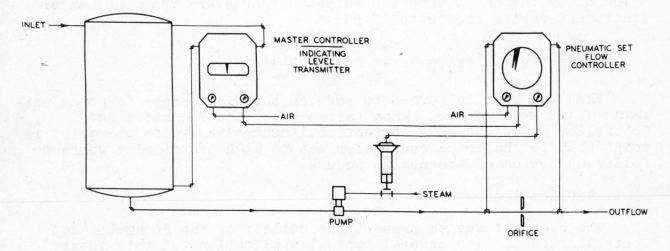

Fig. 143 - Liquid Level Control Using Pneumatic Set
Courtesy of Taylor Instrument Companies

Pneumatic Set Controllers and master controllers with adjustable sensitivity and automatic reset make interesting combinations.

Fig. 143 illustrates a system of this type. The problem is to maintain the material withdrawal rate as nearly constant as possible without allowing the tank level to vary excessively. The Master Controller, an Indicating Level Transmitter Controller, is accordingly set in low sensitivity with a slow automatic reset rate tending to return the level to the center of the tank. Ordinarily this level controller would operate the control valve directly, but variations in steam pressure and pumping head would give undesirable variations in flow rate. In order to satisfy the requirement of smooth outflow, a Pneumatic Set Flow Controller is used to regulate the steam valve and the Master Controller sets the flow rate necessary to keep the level at the center of the tank.

The use of a Master Controller for positioning the set pointers of several Pneumatic Set Controllers is illustrated in Fig. 144. In air conditioning work it is often desirable to adjust the temperature of a room in accordance with outside temperature variations to prevent shock usually experienced by persons entering an air conditioned room on a hot day. The controlled temperatures of rooms A and B can

Information Sheet 10

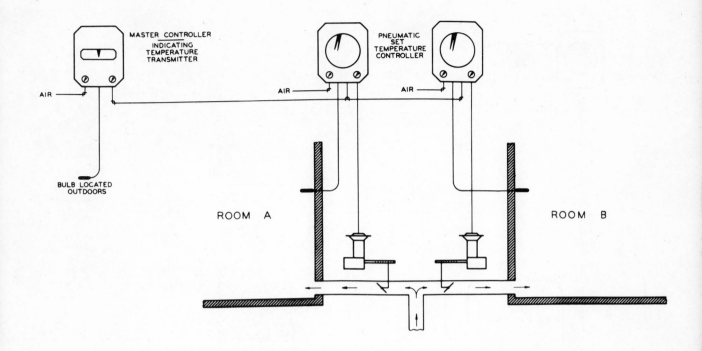

Fig. 144 - Air Conditioning Installation Using Pneumatic Set
Courtesy of Taylor Instrument Companies

be increased a predetermined amount for each degree rise in outdoor temperature above 68°F. by the proper adjustment of the Pneumatic Set Temperature Controllers. In this application, instrumentation is shown for but two rooms. However, a single master Controller may regulate the temperature of as many as fifty or more rooms.

The control application illustrated in Fig. 145 involves the control of the discharge pressure of an air compressor by governing the speed of its internal combustion engine. The process demands upon air compressors are often quite severe, with the result that it is often very difficult, if not impossible, to maintain suction or discharge pressure within close limits without suitable control equipment. The Pneumatic Set Control System applied to an internal combustion engine driven air compressor has proven very successful.

The Master Controller, a Recording Pressure Controller, is equipped with adjustable sensitivity and automatic reset. The instrument sensitivity is adjusted to a relatively high value without sacrificing any stability. The reset rate is adjusted to a value that will cause no deviation between pen and pointer under the most severe load condition. The output pressure from the Master Controller adjusts the set pointer of the Pneumatic Set Pressure

Information Sheet 10

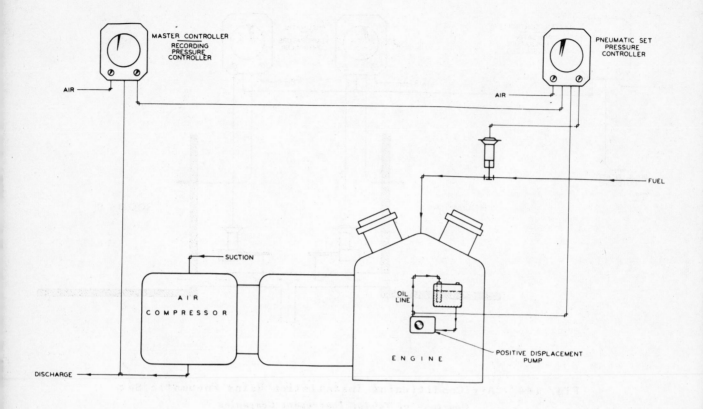

Fig. 145 - Pressure Control Using Pneumatic Set
Courtesy of Taylor Instrument Companies

Controller for the required engine speed to maintain the discharge pressure. The set pointer indicates the speed directly on a square root chart of the Pneumatic Set Controller since the engine speed varies approximately as the square root of the oil pressure from the positive displacement pump which acts as the speed detecting device. The travel of the set pointer is restricted to the safe working band by the limit stops in the pneumatic adjustment unit. In other words, there is a maximum and minimum speed beyond which the set pointer is not to be adjusted.

As the discharge pressure decreases slightly, the output air pressure of the Master Controller changes. This change in output pressure adjusts the set pointer of the Pneumatic Set Controller to higher engine speeds. Since the pen and set pointer are no longer together, the Pneumatic Set Controller increases the opening of the fuel supply valve, and thus increases the speed of the engine to maintain the discharge pressure.

Information Sheet 10

D. Time Schedule Controller

A Time Schedule Controller maintains temperature, pressure flow or liquid level automatically, according to a predetermined time and temperature, flow or liquid level schedule. The controller operates diaphragm valves, lever motors, electro-pneumatic switches, and other diaphragm-operated mechanisms, which in turn regulate the supply of controlling medium to an apparatus. These devices are operated by the controlled flow of compressed air through a pilot air valve in response to the dictates of the cam. The controller mechanism is identical to any standard controller previously described, the added time schedule feature being merely a means for mechanically setting the set pointer.

In the lower case of Fig. 146 the units of the usual Recording Controller are housed. In the upper case the time schedule mechanism is located with connecting link 6 extending to the controller below.

The time schedule mechanism of the basic instrument consists of an electric clock for driving metal cam 2 of which there may be one or two, as desired. Cam follower 5 is connected through link 6 to the baffle movement unit of the controller mechanism, changing the set point (which in the recording controller is done by a hand knob) automatically in accordance with the schedule determined by the contour of the cam and the speed of rotation of the cam clock.

As added features when desired, from one to four trip units may be provided, each including either an air valve, or micro-switch, or both. To operate trip units 1, a metal time disc 7, carrying trip clamps 4, is mounted on the cam clock shaft with the cam. The time disc is imprinted with four time scales, each applying to one of four possible trip units. The trip clamps for each individual trip unit are fastened on the scale pertaining to the same, and in the proper position to operate each trip unit at the desired time without interference one with the other.

When the electric cam clock is used, it may be stopped automatically by a trip unit at the end of the cycle. Cam 2 may then be advanced manually through friction drive 3 to the starting position at the beginning of the next cycle. Such action resets the trip unit for the cycle. Sustained contact push-pull switch 8 keeps the current on unless shut off by hand. If automatic stopping is not desired, the push-pull switch may be used to manually stop and start the cam clock.

In cases where the length of cycle under control, plus the time required for unloading and reloading the apparatus, is greater than the period of rotation of an available cam block, the block may rotate the cam to the starting position after the cycle is completed, and there be automatically stopped by a trip unit. The next cycle may then be started by pressing button 8 of the momentary contact switch and continued by a hold-in relay. This feature also permits

Information Sheet 10

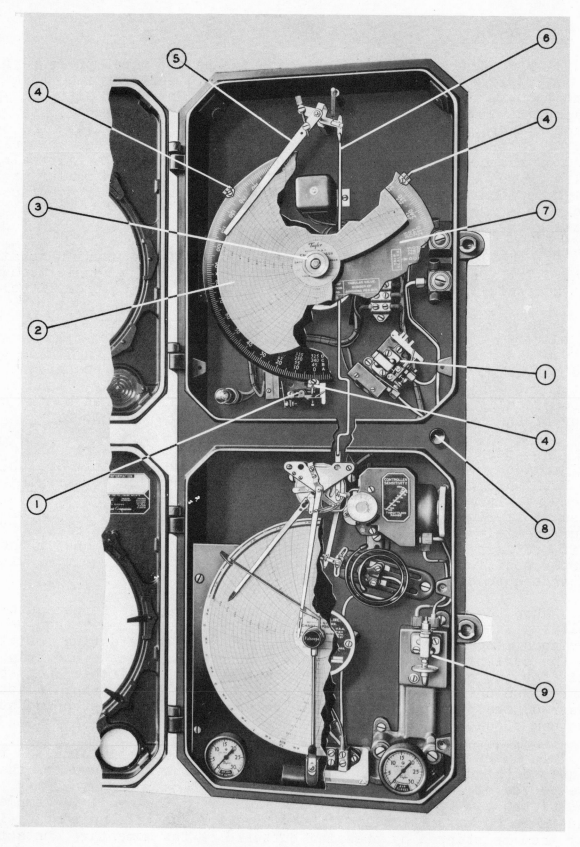

Fig. 146 - Time Schedule Controller
Courtesy of Taylor Instrument Companies

Information Sheet 10

the remote operation of the instrument and the locking of the case
to prevent unauthorized access to the mechanism.

There are several methods of making cams for the Time Schedule
Controller. One method is to glue a Standard Chart to a round steel
or aluminum blank and lay out the desired schedule on the chart.
Another method which is used in making cams is to lay out the schedule on an aluminum or plastic disc upon which is printed a reproduc-
tion of an actual chart. When the complete schedule has been laid
out, the cam is cut with a jig saw, a coping saw, or a metal cutting
band saw. The roughness is removed by use of a file and the edges
are then finished with fine emery cloth.

Cams are quickly and easily interchangeable, and several different schedules can therefore be applied to any one instrument, without
the necessity of individual adjustment.

The cam rotates in a counter-clockwise direction. It actuates
cam follower 5 and connecting link 6 to change the set point of
control mechanism 9 at the lower right. This in turn regulates the
supply of controlling medium to the apparatus under control, resulting in a movement of its recording pen.

Friction drive cam assembly 3 permits the manual rotation of
time disc 7 and cam 7 without loosening the knurled lock-nut. By
loosening the knurled lock-nut, a portion of a turn, it is possible
to shift either cam without disturbing the other.

Information Sheet 11   SPECIALIZED CONTROLLER APPLICATIONS

Size Cooking Control

In the textile industry, the size which is placed on the yarn or warp to produce strength during weaving, and to facilitate weaving by providing a harder surface on the yarn, must be prepared or cooked according to a predetermined time and temperature schedule in order to obtain consistency and other necessary qualities.

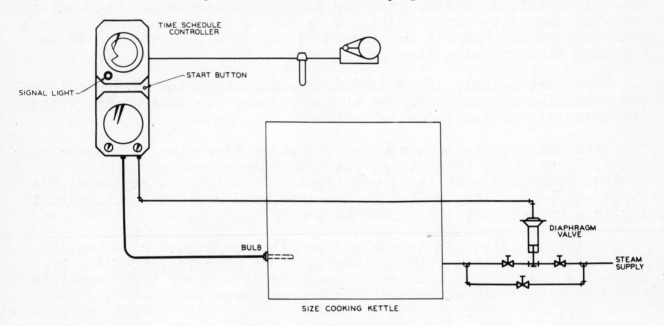

Fig. 147 - Size Cooking Control
Courtesy of Taylor Instrument Companies

In this application, the size is placed in the cooking kettle, Fig. 147, and steam is introduced through perforated pipes in the bottom of the kettle. The temperature is controlled by a Time Schedule Controller with its bulb installed through the side of the kettle.

The Time Schedule Controller is a conventional proportional response instrument operating in relatively high sensitivity whose temperature control point is set automatically by means of a cam. The desired time and temperature schedule is cut on this cam which is rotated by a clock mechanism. The cam follower rides on the periphery of the cam and its motion is transmitted through suitable linkages to the set pointer of the temperature controller. Thus, the temperature follows the schedule as cut on the cam.

The instrument has several accessories to permit fully automatic operation so that it is only necessary for the operator to depress a momentary contact start button. After this operation, the instrument

Information Sheet 11

will rotate the cam and through a trip unit, the air supply will be turned on to the controller which will then actuate the diaphragm valve on the steam supply line to raise the temperature of the contents according to the cam schedule.

The controller then continues the process, raising and holding the temperature for a predetermined period.

As the cam follower reaches the end of the hold period, the trip valve in the upper unit functions to shut off the air supply to the instrument which in turn will allow the normally closed or air-to-open type valve to shut off the steam.

The instrument is so arranged that at this time the cam has returned to the starting position, ready for the next cycle, and at this point, the cam clock automatically stops.

Horizontal Vulcanizer Control

In the rubber industry, certain products are vulcanized in large cylindrical heaters under the influence of live steam admitted to the vulcanizer. In this application, it is generally desirable to raise the temperature to a predetermined value according to a time schedule and to hold it at that value for another time period.

The bulb of the vulcanizer temperature control system, Fig. 148, is installed in a steam circulating pocket external to the vulcanizer. Steam from the inside of the vulcanizer flows through this circulating pocket and its temperature is measured by the bulb. Similarly, an industrial thermometer is installed in order to check the recorded temperature.

As the steam is condensed in the vulcanizer, the condensate is removed by means of the temperature controller whose bulb is installed in a condensate chamber. This control system actuates the diaphragm valve in the condensate outlet line. This, in effect, acts as a thermostatic trap.

The control instrument used is a time schedule controller. The control points of the temperature and condensate control systems are set automatically by means of the cam follower which rides on the periphery of the cam in the upper section of the controller.

In order to start the cycle, it is only necessary to momentarily depress the starting push button which inaugurates the rotation of the cam. The air supply to the control system is turned on automatically by means of a trip valve in the instrument and the controller can then actuate the air-to-open type control valves on the steam supply and condensate outlet lines respectively, thus bringing the temperature of the vulcanizer to the holding period according

Information Sheet 11

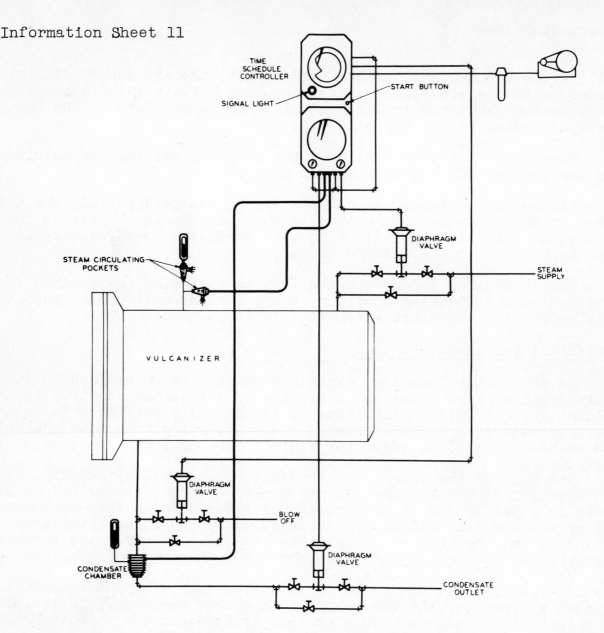

Fig. 148 - Horizontal Vulcanizer Control

Courtesy of Taylor Instrument Companies

to the cam schedule. At the end of the predetermined holding period, the trip valve will again function to shut off the air supply to the control system which allows the two valves to close. Simultaneously, a second trip unit applies air pressure to the blow-off valve which opens to relieve the pressure in the vulcanizer.

A low pressure alarm system consisting of a pressure switch and a buzzer may be provided for a warning in case of air supply failure. Since the vulcanizer has a high heat capacity, the instrument will function in high sensitivity. The effect of load changes, due to the change in product, will therefore not adversely affect the desired schedule.

Information Sheet 11

The entire cycle is automatically controlled and the cam will return to the starting position at the end of a cycle. Here it is ready to continue a new cycle, when the vulcanizer is reloaded, and can be placed in operation by merely depressing the starting push button.

Synthetic Rubber Reactor Control

The synthetic rubber reactor presents a very critical control problem. It involves an endothermic reaction (one which requires heat) during the early stages, and then the reaction becomes exothermic (one which gives up heat), requiring cooling. Near the end of the process, some heat is again necessary.

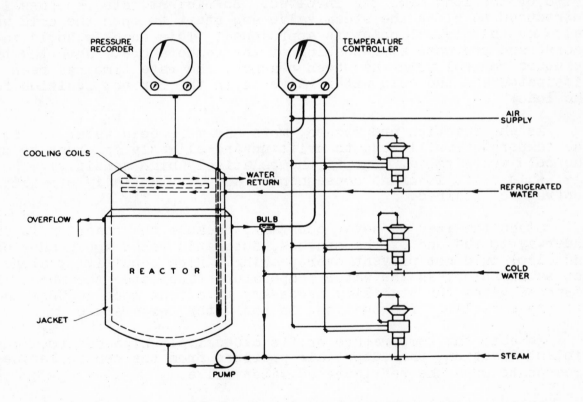

Fig. 149 - Synthetic Rubber Reactor Control
Courtesy of Taylor Instrument Companies

The reactor contents must be brought from charging temperature to reaction temperature quickly and without overpeaking. The bulb of the temperature controller, Fig. 149, is placed in a long well and actuates three diaphragm valves equipped with valve positioners which are installed on steam, cold water, and refrigerated water lines and operate in tandem sequence. The steam or cold water is admitted to the circulating pump to provide the normal heating or cooling. In case of a very violent reaction where the cold water

Information Sheet 11

valve cannot handle the load, the refrigerated water valve opens to admit refrigerated water to the cooling coils in the top of the reactor. The reactor is heated or cooled by the water circulated through the jacket.

Since the time lag in this system is rather long, and since there are violent load changes taking place, it would be assumed that low sensitivity and automatic reset would be required. However, over-peaking of the control point cannot be tolerated, and this will occur with automatic reset. The capacity effect of the reactor is quite high, and by the use of proportional plus rate response, it is possible to obtain excellent results. The sensitivity can be set relatively high, and rate response produces stability. This is in spite of the long time lag involved. Sufficient rate response is introduced to close the steam valve and start to open the cold water valve as the control point is approached. This quickly cools the jacket and prevents over-peaking of the temperature. When the temperature control point has been reached, the rate time has been dissipated and the cold water valve is in the correct position for the load.

As the reaction progresses, more and more cold water is required. The temperature will tend to drift upward slightly in order to open the cold water valve. Due to the relatively high sensitivity possible, this drift is of no consequence, and substantially straight line control is obtained.

Since the load is never constant, because the reaction is always underway to the end of the process, automatic reset would show drift and also could not prevent over-peaking. High sensitivity alone is not satisfactory as the water temperature fluctuates too much. Rate response gives the stability necessary to effect good control and yet prevents large fluctuations in the water temperature.

In case the temperature drifts excessively high due to a more violent reaction, the output air pressure from the controller decreases to open the refrigerated water valve.

An additional tube system with its bulb in the jacket discharge line records the water temperature leaving the jacket.

A pressure recorder records the reactor pressure and can be equipped with an alarm mechanism to sound an alarm in case of high reactor pressure.

Sensitivity is set at approximately 35, and rate time at 2 minutes. Another approach to the reactor problem is the pneumatic set system shown in Fig. 150. As previously mentioned, some drift may be expected when the controller actuates the valves directly. This drift is kept to a minimum by the higher sensitivity possible

Information Sheet 11

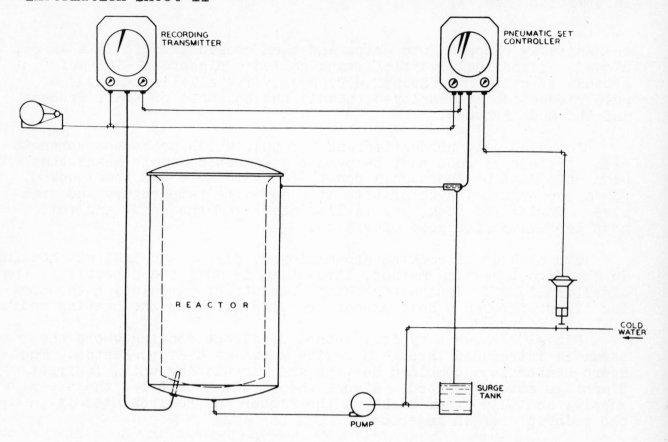

Fig. 150 - Synthetic Rubber Reactor Control Using Pneumatic Set
Courtesy of Taylor Instrument Companies

with the pneumatic set system. In this system, the output air pressure from the Master Controller sets the control point of the Pneumatic Set Controller which directly controls the water temperature. The Pneumatic Set Controller in responding to a demand for a different water temperature, opens or closes the control valves sufficiently to quickly bring the circulating water to a new value which will satisfy the temperature requirements demanded by the master controller The effect of the lag caused by the capacity of the water system is largely eliminated by the use of the pneumatic set system.

Load changes can be largely compensated for with minimum drift of the control point because of the higher sensitivity possible with this system of control. All load changes must be corrected for at the expense of temperature deviation. These load changes are quickly detected and corrected, and the correction is of such magnitude as to show no apparent effect on product temperature.

In this system, sensitivity settings of 50 to 75 are possible, with rate time set at approximately 2 minutes.

Sulphite Digester Control

In the manufacture of wood pulp for paper making, the wood is

Information Sheet 11

mechanically chopped into chips and then cooked in acid in a large, closed, cylindrical, vertical tank called a digester. The acid process is called the Sulphite Process. Two alkaline methods of pulp production are employed, namely the Sulphate or Kraft Process and the Soda Process.

For good pulp production and for pulp which possesses strength each particle of wood must be properly digested. This means that each chip must be thoroughly penetrated with acid and then cooked for a prescribed length of time at a definite temperature and pressure. During the cook, gas is liberated from the acid, and this must be removed for good operation.

Two methods of cooking are employed, direct and indirect heating. In the direct heating method, live steam is admitted directly to the digester liquor. Indirect cooking consists of circulating the cooking liquor through a heat exchanger using steam as the heating medium.

Fig. 151 shows a typical method of direct cooking where the steam is introduced through a device known as a Hydro-Heater. The Hydro-Heater is a combined heating and circulating unit, indirect diaphragm motor operated. A cone shaped disc throttles the steam supply, and this steam picks up the liquor and recirculates it on the principle of an injector.

Temperature and pressure are controlled according to a time schedule as follows:

The bulb of the temperature controller is placed downstream from the Hydro-Heater at a point where adequate mixing has taken place. The pressure connection is attached to the relief line at the top of the digester and pressure is transmitted to the instrument through a seal chamber.

Two Automatic-Manual Control Units are used so that manual operation of the steam inlet and relief valves is obtainable.

In case of an air supply failure, the indirect diaphragm valve closes the steam supply line.

Air pressure can be manually vented from the indirect diaphragm motor in order to shut off the steam supply by operating the three-way cock. During normal operation this cock is in the position shown.

Before starting, air pressure is applied by the Time Schedule Controller trip valve to line E which operates the two three-way pilot valves. Bottom ports B of these valves are closed and ports C are open to admit air pressure to the motor of the relief valve to close it; and to vent air from the indirect diaphragm valve to

Information Sheet 11

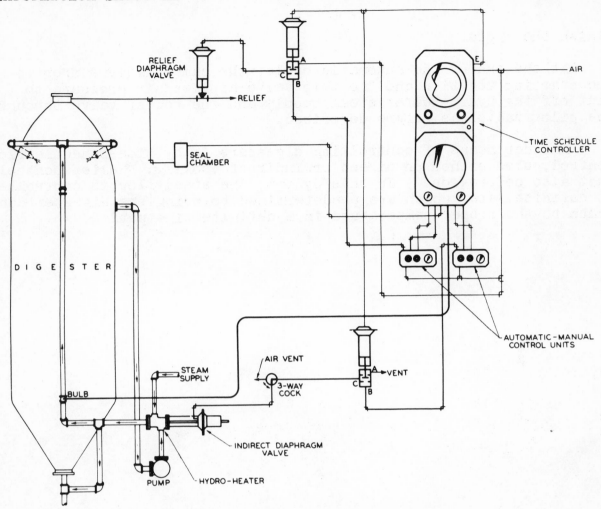

Fig. 151 - Sulphite Digester Control
Courtesy of Taylor Instrument Companies

shut off the inlet steam supply.

To start, the operator depresses the sustained contact push button which starts the cam rotation of the controller. Within 2 angular degrees of the cam rotation, a cam actuated trip valve within the instrument closes, and this reverses the position of the discs in the three-way valves and connects the Time Schedule Controller output air pressures to the indirect diaphragm valve and relief valve respectively. The red signal light in the controller goes on to indicate that steam is being supplied to the digester.

The digester is then brought up to cooking temperature and pressure automatically and according to the predetermined schedules as cut on the temperature and pressure cams.

If, during the cook, it is desired to stop the cam rotation in order to lengthen the cook for any reason, the push button may be operated to open the cam motor circuit, and later closed again to

Information Sheet 11

finish the cycle.

At the end of the automatic cycle, the cam followers drop to the starting position and the trip valve applies air pressure to shut off the Hydro-Heater steam supply and the relief valve through the pilot valves as before described.

Another means of controlling digesters is by time-schedule flow control, used either on direct or indirect cooking. Relief control must also be provided. In this system, the steam flow is controlled at definite rates which are predetermined to bring the digester contents to the proper temperature in a definite time period.

Information Sheet 12   CONTROLLER APPLICATIONS ON FRACTIONATING COLUMNS[*]

Crude petroleum must be subjected to a refinery process in order to secure from it the many products which are of use to us in our daily lives.

In this process the crude oil is run into large iron stills and subjected to the heat necessary for distillation. The distillates which pass off between certain definite temperature limits are separated out and are later purified before being used.

The liquid distilling over from crude oil between temperatures of approximately 70°C. and 150°C. is generally known as naphtha,and that between 150°C. and 300°C. is kerosene. Lubricating oils are taken off at temperatures above 300°C.

A number of naphthas are recognized. Those of low boiling points are called gasoline. Benzine is a naphtha of a high boiling point.

A Pennsylvania crude oil will contain approximately the following products: 4% gas, 30% straight run gasoline, 8% naphtha, 12% kerosene, 8% gas oil, 22% wax distillate and 16% cylinder stock.

Lubricating oils are made by blending the lighter oil obtained from a wax distillate with a heavier component called bright stock, which is secured by filtering and refining the cylinder stock.

Automatic control of the distillation of crude petroleum is but one of the many applications of this type of equipment. However, one glance at the complex distillation equipment in chemical plants, oil refineries, or distilleries with the attendant maze of piping and valves is enough to discourage anyone faced with the problem of applying the correct control instruments. The method of application has often been cut-and-try or duplication of other systems. But cut-and-try can be expensive and duplication of control equipment by no means guarantees results. This information sheet will suggest a better way of approaching the control problems presented by a fractionating column so that the instrumentation may be wisely and economically applied. Instead of considering the whole still system at once, the six principal variables will be considered singly and several possible control systems for each discussed.

First, let us consider the physical principles involved in columns and fractionation.

[*]All illustrations in Information Sheet 12 courtesy of Taylor Instrument Companies.

Information Sheet 12

A. Column Construction

1. Packed Columns

Packed columns, Fig. 152, are probably the simplest type used in industry. They consist of vertical cylindrical vessels filled with irregular material such as crushed coke, stone or rocks or with prepared packing material such as Raschig Rings, which are small, hollow cylinders with equal diameter and length. In a packed column, ascending vapor contacts the film of liquid trickling down the packing. Packed columns are used because of their low initial cost and because packing material resistant to most corrosive substances is available. In operation they sometimes tend to 'channel'; liquid comes down one side of the column and vapor ascends on the other, under which conditions fractionation ceases, so they are sensitive to reflux flow. Another disadvantage is height, since several feet of good packing are only equivalent to one bubble plate, which would require less than one foot of height.

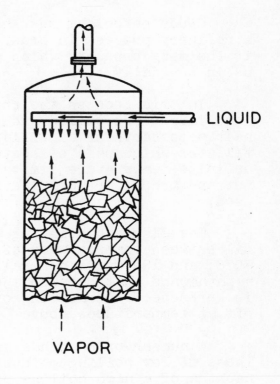

Fig. 152 - A Packed Column

2. Sieve Plate Columns

Sieve plate columns, Fig. 153, have flat perforated plates and downflow pipes. In operation, vapors bubble up through the inch or two of liquid on each plate and liquid descends through the downflow pipes. These columns, generally used only for stripping, are quite sensitive to vapor flow. Too high a vapor velocity blows liquid off the plates; too low a vapor flow allows the liquid to flow through the holes and drain the plates, stopping fractionation. In addition, unless plates are level, such columns are prone to channel. The advantage of sieve plates is that they will handle dense, mucky material which would plug packed columns or bubble plates.

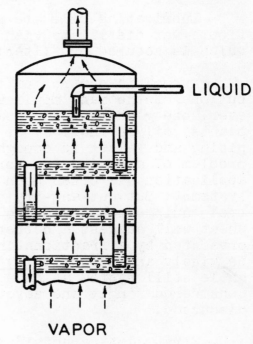

Fig. 153 - A Sieve Plate Column

Information Sheet 12

3. Bubble Plate Columns

The most universally used column is the bubble plate type column,
Fig. 154. Vapor ascends through
riser pipes and bubbles out under
the slotted cap; liquid again descends through sealed downflow pipes.
Most columns, instead of having one
large bubble cap per plate, as shown,
have a great many small ones on each
plate to provide smaller bubbles and
better bubble distribution. These
columns are limited only by the maximum vapor velocity, not by the
minimum.

B. Continuous Distillation Principles

A fractionating column is a device utilizing the difference in
boiling point of two miscible compounds to effect their separation
efficiently into two more or less
pure fractions. The degree of purity

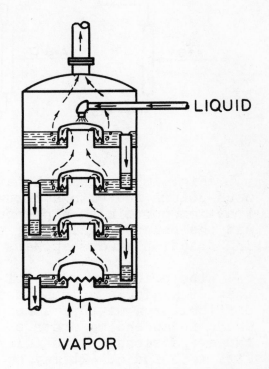

LIQUID

VAPOR

Fig. 154 - A Bubble Plate Column

depends in general upon the number of plates in the column, the
amount of heat used, and the relative volatility of the two components.

Given a problem of separating two components, A and B by
distillation, the purity of both fractions can be increased by
increasing the number of plates in the column or by supplying more
heat per pound of mixture fed to the column.

If it is desired to separate A and B (A boiling at a lower
temperature than B) the mixture is fed somewhere near the middle
of the column and heat supplied at the bottom. In descending from
the feed plate, Fig. 156, the more volatile component, A, is
'stripped' out of B and practically pure B taken out of the bottom.
Above the feed plate, vapors become increasingly richer in A and
poorer in B until practically pure A comes out of the condenser.
In order to get this enrichment of A and throwing down of B, a
part of the A component condensed must be returned to the column
at the top and is called 'reflux'. The operation above the feed
plate is called 'rectification' of fractionation and below the
feed plate, 'stripping'. Though the column may be one type and
size throughout, the portion above the feed plate is called the
'rectifying' section, and that below it, the 'stripping' section.

Information Sheet 12

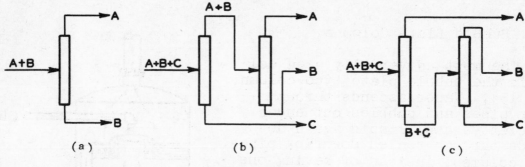

Fig. 155

Fig. 155a shows schematically the flow of material in a continuous column fed with a mixture of A and B near the middle; the fraction containing a preponderance of A being drawn off at the top and the balance, mainly B, coming out the bottom. The higher boiling fraction always appears at the bottom of a column.

The principle of multi-column systems is no more complex than that of a single column though their operation is decidedly more difficult. A mixture consisting of three miscible components A, B and C in ascending order of boiling points may be separated into three fractions in two columns in either of two ways, as shown by Fig. 155b and c. It may be seen that this system can be extended to four components with the separation achieved in three columns.

This rule of two fractions from one column, three fractions from two columns, etc., appears to fall down when additional fractions called 'side cuts' are withdrawn from certain plates between top and bottom of columns. In petroleum refining, side cuts are quite common since petroleum products consist not of pure compounds but of many compounds boiling between certain temperature limits. Side cuts are never pure fractions and generally must be refractionated in separate columns after being roughly separated by the side cut method. This removal of a portion of the reflux from an intermediate plate is analagous to overhead product removal discussed in part D.

C. Column Variables

Fig. 156 represents a typical column separating a mixture into two fractions, the mixture entering at the middle and the fractions being withdrawn continuously at the top and bottom. Heat is supplied at the bottom and cooling medium supplied to the condenser. The column may be operated above, below or at atmospheric pressure.

Any continuous column when operating smoothly should be in a state of dynamic equilibrium. By this is meant that feed enters at a constant rate; A and B fractions are withdrawn at constant rates; heat to the bottom and cooling medium to the condenser are supplied at constant rates. In addition, the composition of material at any

Information Sheet 12

point in the system remains constant and correspondingly the temperature and pressure at any point are constant. Once achieved, a
good equilibrium is a thing to cherish and maintain and is handled
carefully by a good still operator. Any adjustment is made very
slowly and only when necessary. It is the purpose of automatic
control to assist in the maintenance of good equilibrium conditions
despite unavoidable changes.

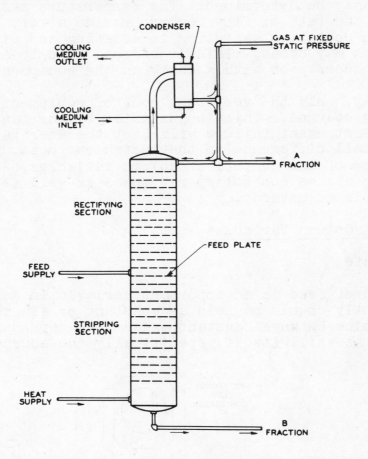

Fig. 156

In a system such as Fig. 156 which represents a well-designed
column running continuously, the following important variables
may be listed:

1. Feed rate.
2. Withdrawal rate of overhead product A.
3. Withdrawal rate of bottom product B.
4. Heat supply rate.
5. Condenser cooling medium supply rate.
6. Static pressure on the column.

These variables will be considered in the above order and in
some detail in part E.

Information Sheet 12

D. Instruments Used on Fractionating Columns

Rate of flow, temperature, pressure and liquid level controllers are required on fractionating columns. While the recording feature is rarely used on the liquid level instruments, it is almost standard to record the other variables. By integrating the record on the rate of flow controllers, the total charge to the column in a given period may be determined. The temperature and pressure records coupled with the rate of flow record provide a very complete story of the column operation assisting in locating and diagnosing any troubles which may occur. This is of real help to an operator and provides his supervisor with a check on the equipment performance.

Generally, only the very best control equipment is used on fractionating columns. This is justified by the fact that poor performance or instrument failure will cost the user far more than the relatively small difference in the instrument cost. In the following discussion of the control of column variables, some indication will be given of the controller responses as well as information regarding their adjustment.

E. Control of Column Variables

1. Feed Rate

The rate of feed is an important variable in column operation and consequently should be held as constant or as smooth as possible. The choice between constant and smooth depends upon conditions external to the still itself, specifically the source of feed supply.

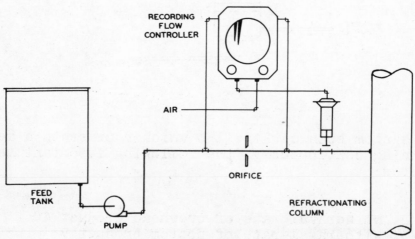

Fig. 157

One condition could be represented by a feed tank of infinite volume, large enough at least so that a flow controller in the feed line, Fig. 157, could be set at the optimum value to maintain a

Information Sheet 12

constant feed rate. This would apply also to semi-continuous systems running for a day or two at a time and stopping when feed supply is exhausted.

Flow controllers with proportional response settings, adjusted to a relatively high sensitivity of 50 psi per inch, are satisfactory in this service but frequently instruments with automatic reset are used. In this case the sensitivity is generally lowered to 20 psi per inch and the reset rate is set between 5 and 2 repeats per minute.

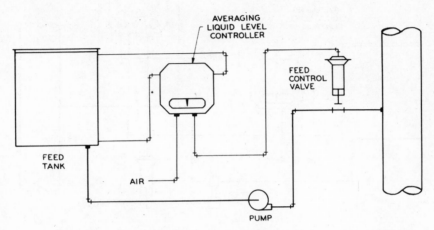

Fig. 158

A more common condition is one where feed is supplied from a tank which itself is fed from another still or from another portion of the process. In this case the problem is to balance the feed rate with the flow to the feed supply tank, making the slowest and smallest possible adjustments in feed rate to the still without allowing the feed tank to run over or become empty. An averaging type liquid level controller on the supply tank is used to regulate the feed rate under these conditions, as shown in Fig. 158. Its action is to maintain a constant valve position as long as the feed level is at the middle of the tank. An increasing flow to the tank raises the level and causes the controller to gradually open the feed control valve. This opening continues until outflow just balances inflow. The level then slowly returns to the half-way point.

Properly adjusted, this type of control makes almost the minimum and smoothest changes in the feed rate possible, and still maintains the tank level within limits. Safety stops built into the averaging liquid level controller cause it to make the sudden changes in feed rate necessary when the tank tends to fill or empty beyond the extreme upper or lower limits because of unusual supply disturbances.

Information Sheet 12

The sensitivity of the averaging liquid level controller must
be low, yet it should be high enough to keep the level from reach-
ing a safety stop on normal disturbances.

A sensitivity setting of 1 psi per inch and an automatic reset
rate setting of .2 repeat per minute are not uncommon.

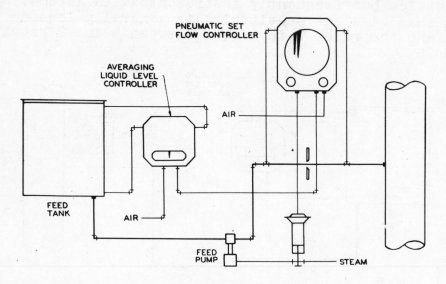

Fig. 159

Certain conditions may call for a slightly more involved flow
control. If, for example, a definite feed valve position did not
necessarily call for a definite feed flow as would be the case if
the valve were regulating a steam pump handling feed, the system
shown in Fig. 159 would be in order. The averaging liquid level
controller on tne feed tank does not directly regulate the steam
supply to the feed pump. Instead, it sets the control point of a
flow controller. A change in feed rate caused by a changing steam
supply pressure or variable other than tank level is corrected
immediately by the flow controller so that a certain output pressure from the averaging liquid level controller calls for a definite
flow rate of feed to the column. This system would also be used
if the feed contained a large amount of solids in suspension, such
as is the case with grain mash.

2. Overhead Product Withdrawal

As previously noted, a portion of the condensed liquid leaving
the condenser is returned as reflux to the top plate. Were none
returned, concentration would not be at the same concentration as
that of the vapors leaving the feed plate. An interchange between
ascending vapors and descending liquid is necessary for either fractionation or stripping.

The quantity of reflux which must be returned to the column

Information Sheet 12

varies with the particular still and with the material being frac-
tionated and may vary between practically zero and 100% of the total
vapors. A very useful term 'reflux ratio' gives the percentage
and is the ratio of reflux to vapor. A reflux ratio of .5 means
that half of the condensed vapors are returned; a reflux ratio of
.9 means that 90% of the overhead is returned as reflux, etc. It
should be noted that reflux ratios in the rectifying section are
always less than one and in the stripping section are always greater
than one.

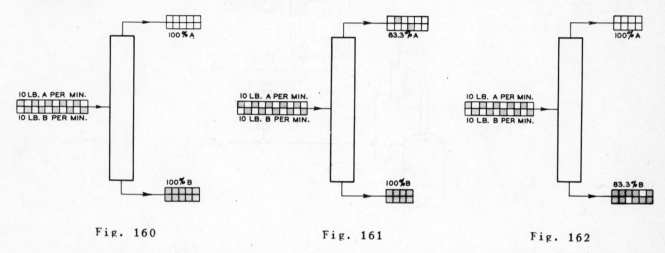

Fig. 160   Fig. 161   Fig. 162

        Although reflux ratios vary widely with different distillations
a simple material balance determines the required rate of overhead
product removal. If a column is to separate a feed consisting of
10 pounds of A and 10 pounds of B per minute into A and B fractions,
Fig. 160, the flow of overhead product cannot exceed 10 pounds per
minute of A, even though 500 pounds per minute is flowing to the
condenser. (Note that fractions A and B cannot be pure compounds
unless the column has an infinite number of plates.) If a greater
quantity, say 12 pounds per minute, is removed, the column must
eventually come to equilibrium with 10 pounds of A and 2 pounds of
B in the overhead product. The concentration would thus fall from
100% A to 83.3% A, Fig. 161. If only 8 pounds of B are removed,
the bottom product will fall to 83.3% B, Fig. 162.

        In other words, overhead product cannot be removed faster or
slower than it is entering in the feed without changing its concentration or that of the bottom product.

        It may then be said that an increased rate of overhead product
removal tends to decrease the overhead concentration and vice versa.
An increased feed flow with corresponding greater through-put of A
will require a greater removal rate, if the same concentration is
to be maintained.

        The problem of overhead product control is, in nearly all

Information Sheet 12

cases, one of withdrawing at the rate necessary to maintain a constant composition. Not temperature, not pressure, but composition.
If a 98% A mixture is desired from the top of a column and the composition falls to 97% it is necessary to reduce the withdrawal
rate. An increase to 99% A means that the product flow should be
increased in order to return to a 98% A product.

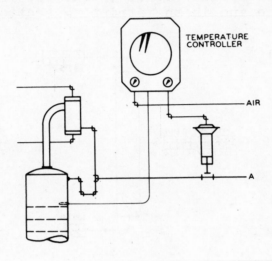

Fig. 163

Since the control problem is one of regulating the product
flow to maintain a definite composition, some quantity which is
a direct measure of composition must be chosen. This is usually
temperature. Fig. 163 shows the simplest overhead product control
system which is adequate in many cases. Figs. 164 to 168 show
other systems which are sometimes used.

The control valve may be located in the product line as shown
or in the reflux line, preferably the former, because in this location fluctuations in liquid flow out of the condenser caused by
erratic heat supply or erratic boiling in the column do not affect
the draw-off rate and consequently the reflux ratio above the
feed plate.

While the controller can be adjusted to a relatively high
sensitivity, it is customary to use automatic reset with proportional
response on this application to obtain the desired accuracy. The
sensitivity setting is in the neighborhood of 20 psi per inch and
the automatic reset setting is usually near .2 repeats per minute.

In order to determine the best control system it is first
necessary to establish the accuracy desired; for example, 96% to
98% of A fraction. Next, from the tables the difference in the
boiling points of the two limiting mixtures is determined, say it
is 1°F. at the pressure existing on the top plate. This should be

Information Sheet 12

enough temperature difference upon which to base control. Less than
1/2°F. is generally insufficient for the system of Fig. 163.

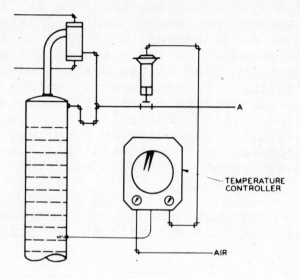

Fig. 164

Quite often, when fairly pure fractions are being produced, the
temperature change at the top plate is entirely too small but at
some point lower in the column a considerable change in temperature
occurs as the overhead varies between the predetermined limits of
concentration. In this case, it is possible to locate the bulb of
a temperature controller at a point perhaps 10 plates down from the
top and regulate the overhead withdrawal to maintain the composition
at this point. See Fig. 164. This control is somewhat more indirect, and relies for its success on the premise that for each temperature measured, a definite equilibrium is being maintained in
the column and that a definite overhead composition exists. It
should be noted that automatic reset and rate responses are almost
necessities in the controller of Fig. 164.

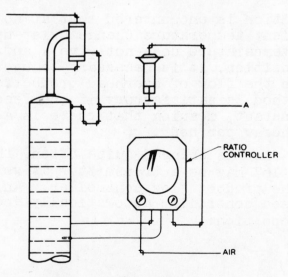

Fig. 165

Information Sheet 12

Boiling temperature is a direct measure of composition only when the pressure at which boiling occurs is known. For this reason it is necessary to consider pressure variations in the column at points of temperature measurement. In Fig. 164 it may readily be seen that an increased vapor flow up the column will occasion a rise in pressure at the plate on which the bulb is located with a corresponding rise in temperature even though the composition remains constant. If pressure variations are appreciable in their effect on the boiling point, it is necessary to compensate for them by means of a ratio controller, Fig. 165, arranged so that an increase in absolute pressure gives a corresponding increase in that temperature control point maintaining a constant composition at the point of measurement. This compensation is exact only over a limited range of pressures.

This may also be accomplished on columns running under pressure or vacuum by regulating this variable at the point of temperature measurement.

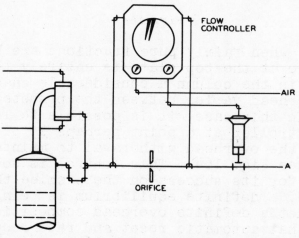

Fig. 166

When the condition is encountered that at no point in the column does sufficient temperature change exist upon which to base control; that is, temperature does not give a sufficiently accurate indication of composition, it is necessary to use still another method and regulate the flow of overhead product directly. See Fig. 166. This method is satisfactory if the feed flow and its composition are constant, meaning that there is a definite quantity of overhead to withdraw per hour.

When the feed-flow is changed quite often, the feed flow controller of Fig. 167 may be a transmitter as well, and set the control point of the product flow controller. An increase of the feed flow by the feed controller automatically increases the product flow in proportion.

Information Sheet 12

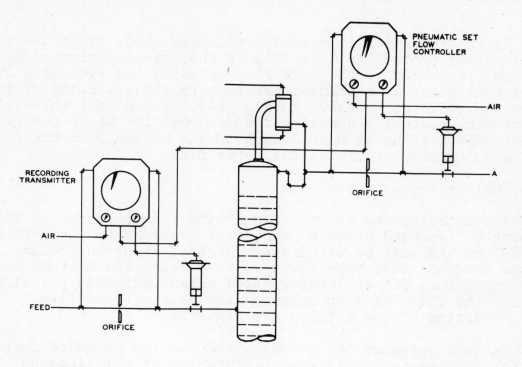

Fig. 167

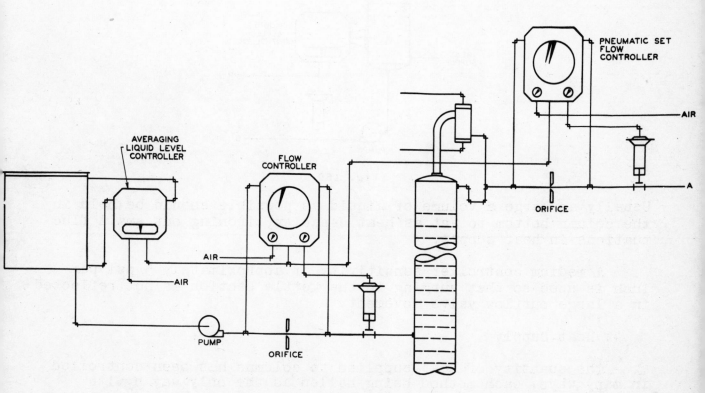

Fig. 168

Information Sheet 12

If the feed flow is varied, as in Fig. 159, by an averaging liquid level controller, the flow of the overhead product may be kept in proportion to the feed flow by using the averaging liquid level controller as a transmitter to vary the set point of the other controllers, as shown in Fig. 168. These last three systems do not compensate for changing feed composition as do the first three. When reflux is pumped back to the column from the condenser the valve usually regulates the refux flow.

3. Bottom Product Withdrawal

All material fed to the column with the exception of that removed as overhead product eventually descends to the bottom of the column and must be withdrawn. Regardless of the column design, bottom products must be removed as they reach the bottom, so this problem becomes one of level control which indicates principally whether the flow out just balances the rate of down flow to the kettle section of the still. See Fig. 169.

On some columns, the actual level carried is quite important in that the heating coils must be immersed at all times but the level must not rise enough to flood the lower plates of the column.

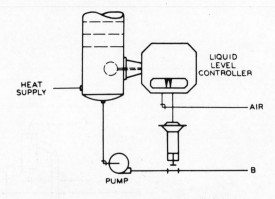

Fig. 169

Usually as large a volume of liquid as possible should be held in the column bottom to act as heat capacity, ironing out small fluctuations in heat supply.

A medium controller sensitivity of approximately 5 psi per inch is used so that surging in the kettle section is not reflected in a large outflow valve movement.

4. Heat Supply

The quantity of heat supplied to columns has been controlled in many ways, each method being hailed as the only way by its proponents. In reality, most of these methods are based on limitations of the columns themselves and are not as universally

Information Sheet 12

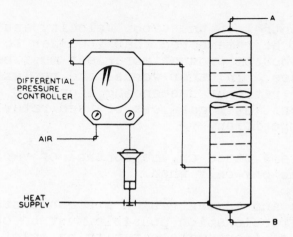

Fig. 170

applicable as are claimed. One method, widely used and perfectly
sound in its place is that of heating to maintain a fairly constant
vapor flow up the column, using the pressure drop over the column
as a measure of flow, as shown in Fig. 170. Or, if the pressure
is atmospheric at the condenser, a straight pressure controller,
Fig. 171, will accomplish the same result. Controller sensitivities
will be quite high.

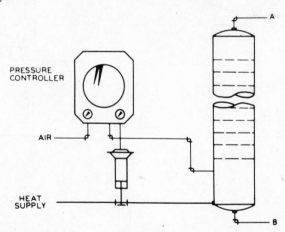

Fig. 171

The pressure drop over a column is the sum of the static pressures due to the heads of one and one-half inches of liquid on the
plates plus the vapor friction drop. The static pressure remains
essentially constant so variations in friction pressure drop are a
measure of the vapor velocity up the column.

The capacity of most columns is limited by the maximum vapor
velocity which can be tolerated; velocities beyond a certain maximum blow liquid upward with the vapor and either 'puke' the column
or nullify the fractionating efficiency of the plates.

Information Sheet 12

Obviously control of the vapor velocity assists in column operation but it must be remembered that in order to maintain the same
concentration of bottom product more heat must be furnished when
feed flow increases. In other words, the reflux ratio in the stripping section, the ratio of descending liquid to ascending vapor,
must be almost constant regardless of feed rate, but must vary with
changing feed composition.

Control systems based on the control of vapor velocity, therefore, are satisfactory only when:

1. Feed rate and concentration are constant.
2. All the fractionation possible must be obtained from
   a column of inadequate capacity by maintaining the
   vapor velocity at a maximum.

In a column capable of producing the necessary stripping at
vapor velocities below a maximum, control of bottom concentration
is most economically obtained by adding only enough heat to strip
the feed to this concentration.

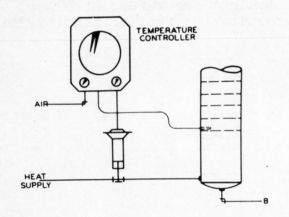

Fig. 172

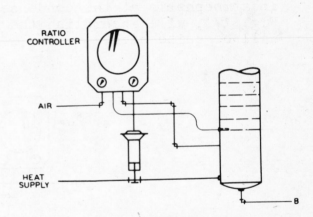

Fig. 173

Applying the same reasoning as on overhead product control, a
variable, usually temperature, is picked which gives a reasonably
true picture of bottom product concentrations. Again, if a temperature change of more than 1/2°F. occurs in the bottom product
boiling point between the allowable concentration limits, temperature control of the heat supply is ample, provided the pressure
changes occuring at the point of measurement do not appreciably
affect the temperature-concentration relationship. See Fig. 172.
Larger pressure fluctuations may be compensated for by the use of
a ratio temperature controller adjusted by absolute pressure, as
shown in Fig. 173.

When quite pure fractions are being withdrawn as bottoms,

Information Sheet 12

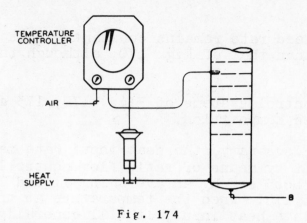

Fig. 174

insufficient temperature changes may occur at the point of withdrawal, but quite frequently a bulb located at a higher plate but
below the feed plate, gives good temperature changes for small
variations at the bottom. This control may or may not be pressure
compensated, depending upon the magnitude of the temperature variation occasioned by the pressure changes. See Fig. 174. Controller
sensitivity will still be quite high.

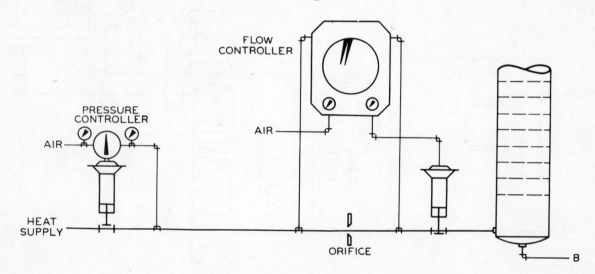

Fig. 175

When insufficient temperature variations occur below the feed
plate, it becomes necessary to fix the stripping-reflux ratio by
flow regulation. When feed flow is constant, this may be accomplished by directly controlling the flow of heating medium, as
shown in Fig. 175. Steam is the usual heating medium and since it
is compressible, a constant flow will be obtained only when its
static pressure is reasonably constant. A reducing valve is used
in Fig. 175 to maintain a uniform steam pressure to the flow controller orifice. Such a control system will hold a uniform flow of
steam to the still whether it goes to heating coils or is injected
directly and consequently maintains a uniform stripping reflux ratio

Information Sheet 12

as long as the feed rate remains constant. This is generally a
better control than that of Fig. 170, although their result is the
same.

Only the control systems of Figs. 172, 173 and 174 compensate
for changing feed composition.

When feed flows vary, the heat input rate may be varied an
equivalent amount by means of ratio flow controllers on the steam
and feed lines, both set by an averaging liquid level controller,
as shown in Fig. 176. When the temperature at the top of a column
is used to regulate heat input, it will generally be found that the
column is used only for stripping. In this case, feed enters on
the top plate which now becomes the feed plate and the control is
the same as that shown on Fig. 174, but with the bulb at the feed
plate.

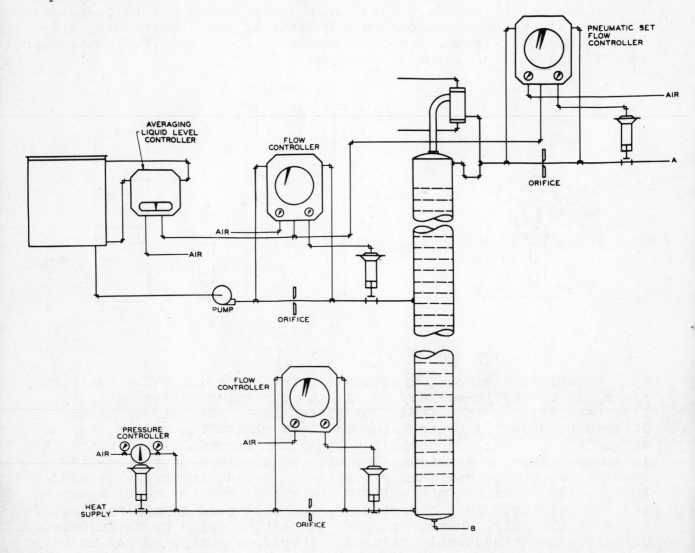

Fig. 176

Information Sheet 12

5. Condenser Cooling Medium Supply

Overhead vapors are usually condensed in some type of surface condenser using water as a cooling medium, though oil, cold brine, or the still feed itself may be used. For purposes of discussion it will be assumed that water is used and that it is desired to condense and cool the overhead vapors to a temperature between that of the cooling water and the vapors; too little cooling water will not cool the product sufficiently, and excessive cooling will waste water or require later reheating of the overhead product.

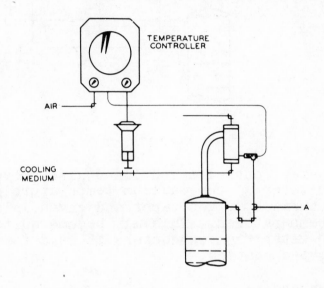

Fig. 177

The problem of condenser water control is usually to put just enough water through the condenser to condense all the vapors and to cool the condensate to the desired temperature. This may be accomplished by regulating the flow of water according to the temperature of the overhead product immediately adjacent to the condenser as shown in Fig. 177. Although this system appears simple, it should be noted that controller sensitivities will be quite low unless the product temperature is very nearly that of the entering condenser water. Automatic reset is a necessity and rate response is helpful.

Occasionally two condensers in series are encountered, column feed being used in the first and water in the second. This generally alters neither the condenser water control nor the overhead product removal control. See Fig. 178.

Actually the use of two condensers, especially where water flows in series through both, is uneconomical, in first cost and in efficiency. Happily, double condenser systems have almost disappeared.

Information Sheet 12

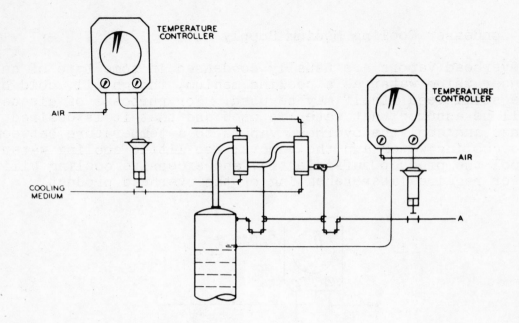

Fig. 178

Condenser water control as outlined also serves to maintain outlet condenser water at the maximum temperature possible with a given condenser surface, given vapor and given inlet water and product outlet temperatures. This may become quite an important consideration if water from condensers is used for boiler feed water or for process heating.

6. Static Pressure

When fractionating low boiling materials, a great many columns operate under pressures above atmospheric in order that condensers may be cooled with water at normal temperatures and that the column capacity be increased by the greater vapor density. Other processes require columns to operate under pressures below atmospheric, either

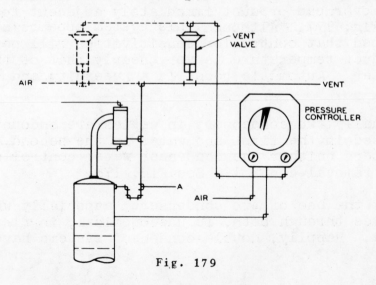

Fig. 179

Information Sheet 12

to increase the fractionation possible or to distill heat sensitive materials at temperatures below their atmospheric boiling point.

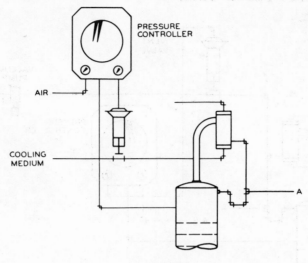

Fig. 180

Control of columns operated at positive pressures usually consists of maintaining a fixed gas pressure in the condenser. Generally some fixed gas, either air or very low boiling material, enters with column feed and must be vented continuously from the condenser. Pressure at any point in the column may be controlled by operation of the vent valve shown in Fig. 179. Controller sensitivity will be high, about 50 psi per inch. Automatic reset is used occasionally when the pressure must be held very constant under wide load variations. Rarely, when no non-condensable gases are present, pressures may be controlled by regulating condenser water flow as shown in Fig. 180. The pressure is controlled by changing the overhead product temperature to change its vapor pressure. This is not the best solution to this case, however. A much better method would be to modify the system of Fig. 179 by constantly bleeding a small amount of air into the system either at the condenser or into the feed pump. Or, if necessary, operate another valve, broken lines of Fig. 179, from the same controller which would admit air if the pressure were below the desired value; the vent valve relieving if the pressure were high.

In sub-atmospheric columns, absolute pressure is generally controlled rather than vacuum, since absolute pressure determines the boiling point equilibrium, and vacuum becomes increasingly more arbitrary at low absolute pressures.

Either dry vacuum pumps, water jet ejectors, or steam jet ejectors are used to remove fixed gas from the system. Each method has the same limitation, namely that the amount of fixed gas pulled out cannot be regulated by varying steam or water flow to the ejectors or the speed of dry pumps. The jets

Information Sheet 12

especially must run at a constant rate of steam or water flow; any attempt to drop below this normal flow causes the jet to lose its ejecting power and 'flash back'.

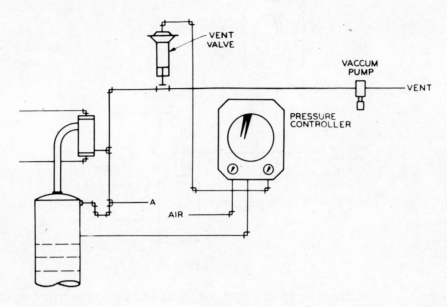

Fig. 181

Control of low pressure columns is accomplished either by regulating the flow of non-condensables from the condenser to the vacuum producing equipment, as shown in Fig. 181, or in adding non-condensables to load the vacuum producers, as shown in Fig. 182.

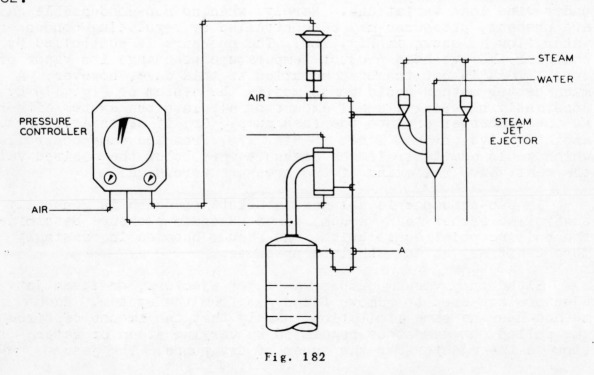

Fig. 182

Information Sheet 12

In the former, the valve is located in the vacuum pump line; in the latter a small valve allows air to bleed into the same line, making up the difference between fixed gas entering the column from feed or leaks, and fixed gas which the vacuum pump will pull at the existing absolute pressure.

F. Batch Distillation Principles

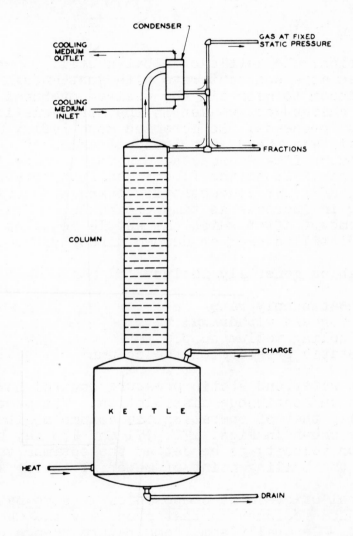

Fig. 183

Batch distillation varies from continuous so little that a brief description will suffice to cover the principles involved. Fig. 183 shows a typical batch still having a kettle, capable of holding a complete charge of feed, surmounted by a column with the conventional condenser and reflux lines. In effect, it is identical to the continuous column of Fig. 156, except that the rectifying section only is retained and the feed space is a great deal larger, so large in fact, that it will hold the entire batch of feed at once.

Information Sheet 12

The principal disadvantage of batch columns is that stationary
equilibrium conditions, so highly esteemed in continuous distillation, are not obtainable in batch work. Composition in the kettle
is continuously changing and consequently altering the equilibrium
throughout the column. Batch stills have the advantages of cheaper
first cost and easier operation, and are used when batches are too
small to justify continuous operation even though efficiency is
sacrificed.

G. Batch Column Variables

In operation, the kettle of a batch still is charged with feed
which is boiled at a constant rate with just enough reflux returned
from the condenser to maintain the desired overhead concentration.
Obviously the charge gets weaker in the more volatile component A
as distillation proceeds. So more and more reflux must be returned
in order to maintain the desired concentration of overhead. Eventually the product flow decreases to a point where it is no longer
economical to distill, so the flow is shifted to another receiver
and a fraction of lower concentration taken off during which the
reflux must again increase as time progresses. Several fractions
may thus be removed after which the kettle contains almost pure B
which may be distilled over or dumped directly from the kettle.

The variables generally include:

1. Heat supply rate
2. Overhead withdrawal rate
3. Cooling medium supply rate
4. Static pressure on the column

Condenser water and static pressure control have been covered
in the section on continuous distillation. The problem of heat supply is generally that of operating the column at its maximum rate
so the methods shown in Figs. 170, 171 and 175 may be used. These
allow the vapor velocity to be set at the optimum value regardless
of changes in the boiling point of material in the kettle.

The control of overhead composition is somewhat different from
that on continuous columns in that product withdrawal rates are
never constant. Generally some temperature change occurs between
fractions so the method shown in Fig. 159 is most widely used. The
controller automatically decreases product flow to maintain the
desired temperature. When vapor flow is controlled at a constant
value, the control valve of Fig. 163 may be located in the reflux
line if more convenient, though the better method is as shown where
surges of vapor flow do not effect the draw-off rate.

At the end of a fraction, marked by a minimum product flow, the
control point is set to the higher boiling point of the new fraction

and so on. It is possible to make a batch distillation completely
automatic by means of a time schedule controller with its cam cut
for the required boiling points and its clock wired in series with
a pressure switch connected to the controller output. Closing of
the product withdrawal valve starts the cam, advances it to a higher
temperature and stops the cam until product flow again drops to a
minimum. A secondary cam may be used to divert each fraction to the
proper receiver.

In some cases it is possible to locate the controller bulb
several plates down from the top when small temperature differences
exist at the top plate. However, due to the shifting equilibrium
in batch stills, this mid-column temperature is usually a poor measure of top concentration and should be used only in special cases.
Automatic reset and rate responses would be necessary if the bulb
were many plates from the top.

H. Typical Fractionating Column Control

Fig. 184 is a typical illustration of the instrumentation required on a petroleum fractionating column. This particular control
system is used most often on gasoline and distillate stabilizers in
which the light ends (higher boiling point fractions) are distilled
off to improve the product.

On this particular installation, a buoyancy type liquid level
controller is placed on the accumulator, which receives the distillate from a previous fractionating unit. This buoyancy type level
controller adjusts the control point on a flow controller, having
its valve in the feed line to the stabilizer. As the level rises,
the set point on the flow controller is moved upward gradually to
increase the feed, and as the level falls, the set pointer is moved
downward. The sensitivity setting on the level controller is generally about three psi per inch (100% throttling range) so that the
feed varies gradually as the level in the accumulator changes.
Sudden changes in rate of feed must be avoided to prevent upsetting
the equilibrium in the stabilizer.

On some installations, the level controller is used to operate
the valve in the feed line directly. This is a satisfactory and
more inexpensive substitute for the system illustrated, and no
trouble is experienced if a valve positioner is used on the valve.
The pneumatic set flow controller provides a record of the feed to
the unit, which is always desirable, and in addition eliminates
the need for the precisor.

A ball float type level controller is illustrated on the reboiler, although a buoyancy type unit or manometer type level controller may be used equally well. Since the product is most often
taken to storage, this controller may have a very narrow throttling

Information Sheet 12

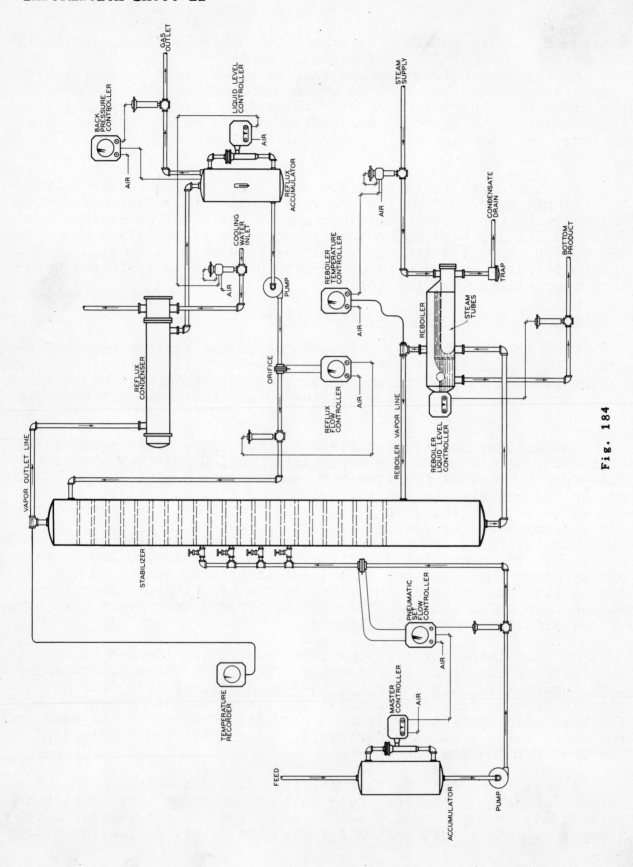

Fig. 184

range and therefore may be of a relatively simple type. The temperature control on the reboiler operates a valve in the steam line leading to the tube bundle. Due to the time lag which exists on this particular application, the instrument sensitivity must be moderately low so that this instrument is most often equipped with automatic reset, and a valve positioner is recommended for the diaphragm valve.

A simple recorder is used for the top tower temperature and its bulb is located in the vapor outlet line. The main purpose of this recorder is to make sure that the column is operating properly and that the heavier fractions (high boiling point fractions) do not distill over the top. A simple flow controller is shown in the reflux line to the top tower. Generally this instrument has only a proportional response, and its set point is adjusted to maintain a satisfactory reflux ratio. In actual practice, the setting on this instrument and the temperature which results in the top of the column depend upon the analysis of samples taken from the reflux accumulator. Since most stabilizers are operated under pressure, this is maintained by a back pressure controller having its valve in the outlet gas line. This is a simple control application and can generally be handled by an instrument with a relatively high sensitivity. Automatic reset is not required, due to the capacity in the system.

The buoyancy type level controller on the reflex accumulator controls a valve in the water line to the reflux condenser. If the level in the accumulator increases, the flow of water is reduced, and a smaller percentage of the overhead product is condensed. Therefore, it will be noted that the entire overhead product eventually must be withdrawn through the gas line. The industrial thermometer on the reflux accumulator is of assistance in stabilizing the operation.

In general, control systems are individually tailored for each job. The systems are varied and depend upon the requirements of each application. Therefore, the system illustrated should only be considered as typical of a particular field.

J. Summary

Fractionating columns whether perforated plate, bubble plate, or packed columns are simply devices for effecting a counter current interaction between liquid and vapor in order to separate efficiently a mixture of two mutually soluble liquids into two fractions of different composition.

Fractionation separates mutually soluble substances of different boiling points. A process called steam distillation, not covered in this section, purifies mixtures such as peppermint oil

Information Sheet 12

and water which are only slightly soluble.

Stripping occurs below the feed plate and drives the more volatile material out of the less volatile fraction.

Rectification occurs above the feed plate and concentrates the more volatile fraction. Reflux is returned to the top plate giving the downward flow of liquid necessary to wash the less volatile material out of the volatile fraction.

Equilibrium conditions in continuous columns should be as stationary as possible. Equilibrium means the temperature or concentration gradient from point to point in the column.

Column controls might be divided into primary and secondary classifications. Those of primary importance regulating the concentration of overhead product and bottom product; secondary, including feed rate, bottom outlet, condenser water and static pressure. All of these variables must be controlled automatically or manually.

Good fractionating column controls will do some or all of the following:

1. Save labor.
2. Save heating medium.
3. Save cooling medium.
4. Give the exact fractionation required.
5. Give maximum fractionation possible for a given column. (Vapor velocity control)
6. Make possible good operation of multi-column stills too involved for adequate manual control.

Information Sheet 13   CONTROLLER APPLICATIONS ON HEAT EXCHANGERS

Tube Still Control (Gas Fuel)

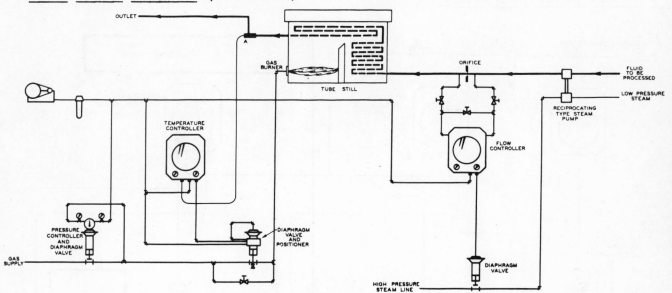

Fig. 185 - Tube Still Control
Courtesy of Taylor Instrument Companies

A tube still, Fig. 185, is an apparatus for adding heat to a fluid to partially vaporize it. Tube stills are very common in the oil refining industry.

The temperature control problem is to maintain a substantially constant outlet temperature from the tube still by varying the flow of fuel to the burners. The bulb of the temperature controller is located at the still outlet, and the control valve and positioner are installed in the gas (or oil) fuel supply line. A pressure controller is generally used to control the gas pressure upstream from the control valve.

Flow of the fluid to be processed is controlled by an orifice type flow controller which varies the amount of steam admitted to the reciprocating type steam pump.

The time lag on a tube still is appreciable, and as a result, low sensitivity is a requirement. Load variations are frequent and of considerable magnitude, which add to the control problem. Among the load changes are variations in the BTU content of the gas fuel, draft at the burners, radiation and convection, and composition of the change. These are not readily controlled and must be compensated for by the control system.

Automatic reset and rate response are used to provide load compensation and quick recovery of the control point when load changes occur. As a result of automatic control on tube stills there are big savings in labor, greater output, better efficiency, uniform quality and fuel savings.

Information Sheet 13

Juice Heater Control

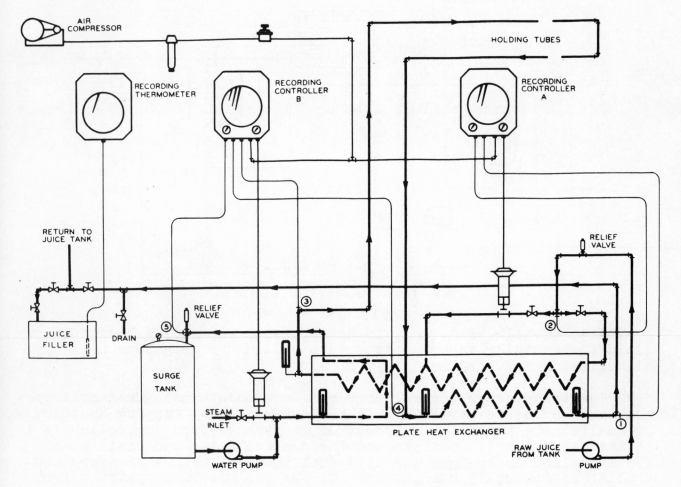

Fig. 186 - Juice Heater Control
Courtesy of Taylor Instrument Companies

In processing fruit and vegetable juices one of the critical
points in the process which determines the flavor and the keeping
qualities of the juice is the juice heater or pasteurizer, Fig.
186. Probably the great majority of heaters in the field are low
temperature pasteurizers, but more recently there has been a tendency to heat the juices to a higher temperature for a shorter time
interval. It is claimed that with this system the retention of
flavor is better and satisfactory sterilization is accomplished.

A suitable control system has been developed utilizing a plate
heater and standard instruments. Raw juice is pumped into the heat
exchanger, part of it being used to cool the pasteurized juice leaving the exchanger. Single duty, bi-record temperature controller,
A, controls the temperature of the juice leaving the exchanger by-
passing the necessary portion of the raw juice entering the heater.

Information Sheet 13

The juice then passes through the balance of the exchanger where its temperature is brought up to the final desired value. This is accomplished by means of a water circulating system in which the water is heated by the direct injection of steam. The diaphragm valve in the steam line is controlled by Recording Controller B with bulb 3 in the juice leaving this portion of the heat exchanger.

The hot juice passes through the holding tubes which are of a suitable length to produce pasteurization and bulb 4 of the temperature controller records the temperature of the juice returning to the exchanger. The third bulb 5 of Recording Controller B records the temperature of the water in the circulating system. After the juice is cooled to the desired filling temperature, it passes on to the filler. A recording thermometer indicates the temperature in the filler at all times.

In juice pasteurization, it is sometimes desirable to use temperatures above the boiling point of water at atmospheric pressure. Therefore, the water surge tank is a closed vessel and a pressure relief valve is provided. The relief valve must be set at a pressure high enough to permit a suitable temperature differential between the water and the hot juice. Since the juice in the holding tubes may be above 212°F., the subsequent cooling of it is essential for satisfactory operation.

Automatic reset is used in the temperature controllers to compensate for load changes due to inlet juice temperature variations, rates of juice flow, and steam pressure variations.

Short-Time Pasteurizer Control

In the short-time high temperature pasteurization of milk products, adequate and accurate temperature control is most important. The milk must be heated to a temperature which completely pasteurizes the product and which is always above a certain legal minimum specified by health authorities, and yet be not over-heated, which would result in a detrimental effect on the quality of the product. This application represents a typical case where the apparatus has been designed properly with respect to heat transfer, time lag, etc., in order to produce a unit which readily lends itself to automatic control. In other words, the equipment has been designed with the end in view of permitting simple, accurate and dependable instrumentation.

The pasteurizer, Fig. 187, consists of four sections, namely: the regenerator, heater, holder tube, and cooler section. The raw milk enters the milk surge tank and from this point passes through the regenerator section where it is partially heated by the outgoing hot milk from the holder tube. The milk is pumped from the milk surge tank through the regenerator section and through the

Information Sheet 13

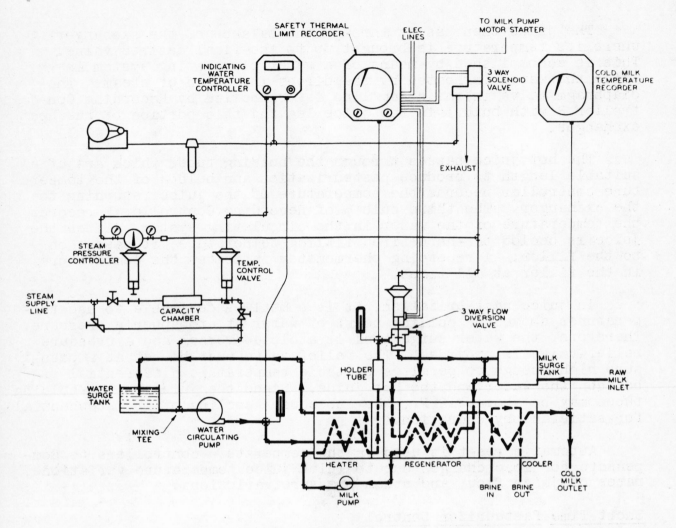

Fig. 187 - Short-Time Pasteurizer Control
Courtesy of Taylor Instrument Companies

final heater section where it is heated by circulating hot water.
From the heater section, the milk passes through a long holder tube
which is of sufficient length to permit the milk to be held at its
pasteurizing temperature for a definite length of time. The holder
tube is so designed that when the milk is pumped at a constant rate,
it will be held at the proper temperature for the correct length
of time. The milk then passes through a flow diversion valve back
to the regenerator section where it gives up some of its heat to the
incoming cold milk and then is finally cooled in the cooling section
by brine circulating through the section.

Short time pasteurizer equipment is generally of the plate type
where one medium flows counter-current to the other between thin
plates. This design permits a rapid transfer of heat and also permits ease of taking the unit apart for cleaning.

The safety thermal limit recorder is an instrument of special

construction for this particular application and serves as a safety
device. It actuates the flow diversion valve through the 3-way
solenoid valve to divert the flow of milk from the holding tube
back to the raw milk surge tank, in case the temperature at the
outlet of the holding tube drops below the legal minimum. As long
as the temperature is at the proper pasteurizing point, the flow
diversion valve will be in such position as to allow the milk to
flow forward through the regenerator section and then on to the
cooling section and the bottling machine. The operation of the
safety thermal limit recorder system will not be further discussed
here as its only function is as described above, except that it does
give a record of the outlet milk temperature.

The milk temperature is controlled indirectly by maintaining
the water inlet temperature at a given value by the indicating water
temperature controller with its bulb located in the outlet from the
water circulating pump. This instrument actuates the temperature
control valve and thus regulates the quantity of steam necessary for
maintaining a constant water temperature.

When the temperature of the milk at the holding tube outlet is
below the set point of the safety thermal limit recorder as it is
during the starting period, or in cases of emergency, the 3-way
solenoid valve shuts off the air to the flow diversion valve and
diverts the milk back to the surge tank. The steam pressure controller also receives its air supply from the 3-way solenoid valve,
and, therefore, during these periods, the steam pressure control
valve is wide open. This allows full steam pressure to be applied
ahead of the temperature control valve to accelerate heating while
milk is being diverted to the surge tank. As soon as the pasteurization temperature is reached, forward flow again takes place, and
air pressure is admitted to the steam pressure controller which then
controls the steam supply pressure at the optimum pre-determined
value. This pressure is usually about 15 psi below the minimum
line or boiler pressure available.

Since the flow of milk through the pasteurizer must be constant,
adequate temperature control is provided by controlling the circulating water temperature which heats the milk. The heating water is
circulated rapidly through the heater section from 4 to 6 times as
fast as the milk is passing through. This rapid circulation cuts
down time lag with the result that the water temperature controller
will operate in a fairly high sensitivity. Thus, the milk temperature is controlled uniformly by maintaining a constant water inlet
temperature.

In case the milk pump is shut down, the water temperature will
tend to increase due to the no-load condition, but because of the
relatively high instrument sensitivity, it will not increase
excessively to shut off the steam supply to the circulating water

Information Sheet 13

system.   The milk in the heater will increase in temperature to approximately that of the water.

The advantage of the use of a separate steam pressure controller on applications such as this is two-fold.   In the first place, it eliminates the effect of load changes from varying boiler pressure, and in the second place, provides a means for setting the pressure at the best value with respect to the opening of the temperature control valve, thus permitting in effect a means for having the proper size temperature control valve for the existing load condition.

The outlet cold milk temperature is recorded by the cold milk temperature recorder.

Information Sheet 14   CONTROLLER APPLICATIONS IN INDUSTRIAL
                       AIR CONDITIONING

Air conditioning and indoor comfort mean the same thing to many persons. Occasionally one hears of an air conditioned building being so cold in the summer that the difference in temperature experienced when passing from the out-of-doors into the building comes as a distinct shock to persons making the change. Those who remain within the building, however, feel no discomfort. Hence, there is a difference in the degree of comfort experienced by a person remaining continuously indoors in a room at 70°F. and that experienced by a person who must alternate between outdoor and indoor temperature conditions. Conditions for optimum summer comfort for those who are indoors for three hours at a time or less will therefore depend somewhat on the outdoor temperature.

Since the temperature of the human body is usually higher than that of the surrounding atmosphere, heat is constantly being given off to the air. Heat is also being given off by the body for evaporation of perspiration.

Because the rate of evaporation will vary with the ability of the air to absorb moisture, a person will feel warmer at the same room temperature when the relative humidity is high than he will under the same conditions with a low relative humidity. The rate of evaporation is also increased by an increase in the rate of movement of the air. Thus since temperature alone is not responsible for feeling 'hot' or 'cold', an arbitrary temperature value known as the 'effective temperature' which takes into account such factors as the relative humidity, the amount of air movement and the actual temperature is used by heating plant engineers.

The body makes certain physiological adjustments which enable it to withstand lower temperatures in the winter than in the summer. This, coupled with the fact that one usually wears heavier clothing in the winter than in the summer makes it necessary to provide two entirely different temperature ranges: one for winter comfort and one for summer comfort.

This may be accomplished automatically by providing a control system whose response depends upon the outdoor temperature as well as that within the controlled rooms.

A system of this type will provide more heat on cold days and less on warmer days and tends to overcome the effect of heat transmission losses through the walls, floors, and roof of the building.

Uninsulated outer walls of a room may remain cold after the air temperature has risen to a point which should give comfort. The uncomfortable feeling of cold may persist because of radiation to these walls. To overcome this effect, systems of heating which

Information Sheet 14

place the heating pipes at regular intervals within the walls or the floors of the building have been developed and are proving to be of value. Systems of this type are sometimes called panel heating systems.

Manufacturers of air conditioning equipment are confronted with innumerable problems. It is difficult to maintain a satisfactory temperature in a night club where part of the people are dancing and part of them are seated. A comfortable temperature for those dancing is too cool for those seated. The question of what is meant by an air conditioner is not fully understood by everyone. A man may buy a house in which an air conditioner is installed and then discover that it is only a winter air conditioner when he expected that it would provide year-round air conditioning. The expense of summer air conditioning has delayed its general adoption for general residential use.

Automatic controllers and recorder controllers are well adapted for use with commercial air conditioning systems.

The following installation diagrams will show a few controller applications to air conditioning systems.

Print Shop Air Conditioning Application

Fig. 188 illustrates an air conditioning system which was designed for a print shop. In this particular case, it was desired to maintain a constant dry bulb temperature of 75°F. and a relative humidity of 45%. Air conditioning in print shops is important since it insures a good registration in multi-color printing operations.

The dry bulb of the Master Controller operates the valve in the steam line to the Reheater. The wet bulb temperature adjusts the control point of the Pneumatic Set Controller which has its bulb in the circulating spray water line. The pneumatic set instrument operates the valve controlling the heat being added to the circulating spray water and a valve in the refrigeration system. The valves are staggered so that both cannot be effective at the same time. When the valve in the cooling coil line is opened, the electro-pneumatic switch puts the refrigeration system in operation. The adjustable three-way valve closes the fresh air and relief dampers when cooling is required. A certain percentage of fresh air is added to the system for ventilation purposes by means of the manually adjusted damper which is not under automatic control. The reverse-acting expansion stem type controller is responsive to the outside air temperature and it closes the fresh air and relief dampers by means of the non-adjustable pilot valve whenever the outside temperature goes below 40°F. Thus the plunger remains in the position shown, except when air to the diaphragm valve line is cut off as the

Information Sheet 14

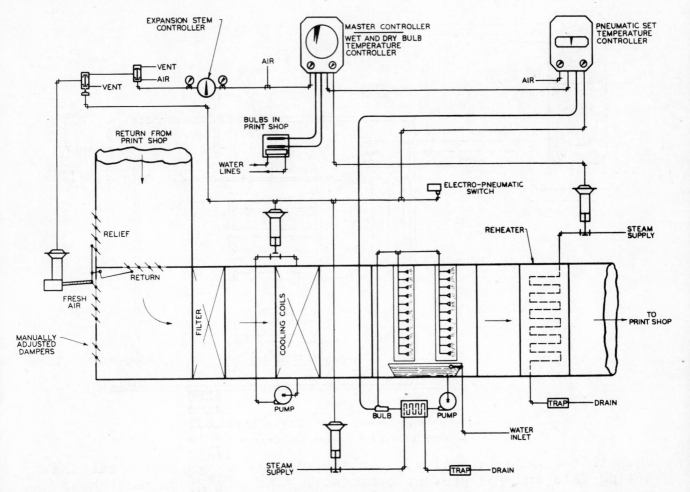

Fig. 188 - Print Shop Air Conditioning Application
Courtesy of Taylor Instrument Companies

temperature drops below 40°F. The purpose of this is to prevent freeze-up in the system.

Many air conditioning jobs do not require cooling or the addition of moisture. Driers of all classes fall into this group. In the simple driers, it is unnecessary to control the relative humidity on the drier. On others, the moisture content as well as the temperature of the air must be carefully controlled.

Compartment Type Drier Application

A compartment type drier is illustrated in Fig. 189. On this particular installation, a time schedule controller is used, and the dry bulb operates a valve in the steam line to a heater. The wet bulb controls a lever motor which operates the dampers. A circulating fan and baffles are used to distribute the air. When the product is introduced into the drier, it is customary to start off with relatively high wet and dry bulb temperatures. As the moisture is evaporated from the surface of the material in the drier, both the wet and dry bulb temperatures are lowered.

Information Sheet 14

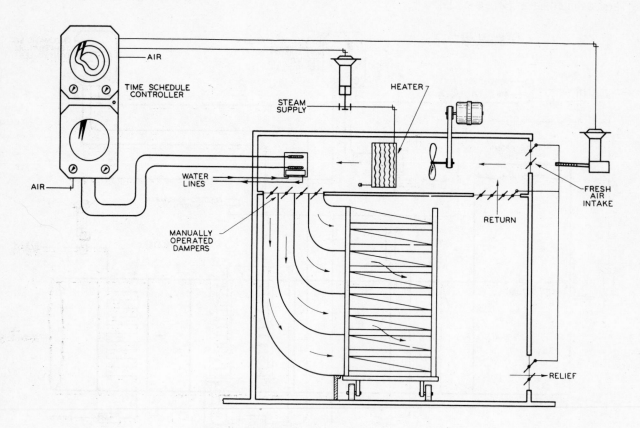

Fig. 189 - Compartment Type Drier Application
Courtesy of Taylor Instrument Companies

When this scheme is followed, it is possible to achieve a maximum drying rate and yet prevent overheating and surface hardening of the product.

The instrument which is used to control the compartment type drier is a time schedule controller with two cams. Two separate temperature controllers are housed in the lower instrument case. One is actuated by the dry bulb temperature to regulate the steam valve and the other is actuated by the wet bulb temperature to control the dampers.

The cams in the upper unit adjust the two set pointers of the lower unit by means of a mechanical linkage. Hence, by shaping and correlating the two cams it is possible to achieve a maximum drying rate at the start of the drying period and yet prevent excessive drying in the final stages.

At the start of the drying process, heat and outside air are both applied until a maximum drying rate is secured. Then the dampers admitting and exhausting outside air may be closed to prevent further drying. At the close of the process these may again be opened to secure the maximum drying rate for a brief period.

This type of system is used widely in the dehydrating of vegetables.

Information Sheet 14

Conveyor Type Drier Application

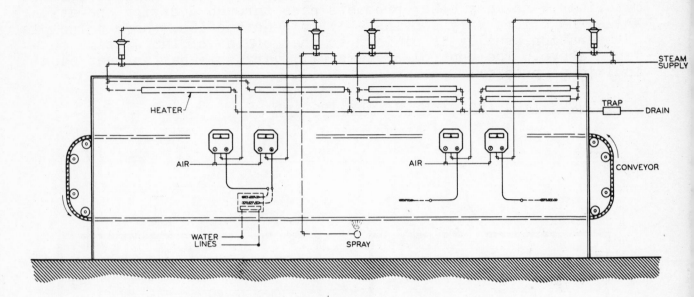

Fig. 190 - Conveyor Type Drier Application
Courtesy of Taylor Instrument Companies

A conveyor belt drier is illustrated in Fig. 190. The material to be dried is placed on a screen-like belt which passes through a tunnel. In general, the tunnel is divided into sections so that the temperature in each particular part can be adjusted to meet the requirements of the particular product. Although it is not shown in the drawing, air is withdrawn from each section of the tunnel at the bottom and recirculated through the top with a certain percentage of fresh air. Driers of this class are used on cotton, rayon, synthetic rubber, and other similar materials.

The product to be dried is fed to the conveyor at the right of the figure. It is carried through the drier and dropped on another conveyor (not shown in the diagram) which carries it to storage or to the next operation.

Very rapid drying is produced by the action of the first two heaters and the temperature beneath them is individually controlled.

To prevent excessive drying, the wet bulb controller in the finish drying end operates a diaphragm valve which admits moisture from a steam line.

The two heaters applying the final drying effect are controlled by the dry bulb temperature controller.

Indicating temperature controllers are shown in the figure, but recording controllers are often used, particularly on the finish end, since this provides a record of the final drying temperature.

Information Sheet 14

There are many other types of driers which are in use indus-
trially today. Paper, lumber, photographic film, textiles, ceramic
materials, and many other products pass through a drying operation.
While the driers vary considerably in construction, their principle
of operation usually is similar to that of one of the systems outlined above. The control systems will vary somewhat to meet each
individual problem.

Continuous Type Tunnel Drier Application

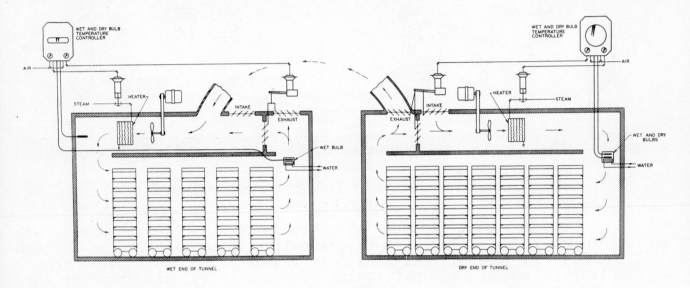

Fig. 191 - Continuous Type Tunnel Drier Application
Courtesy of Taylor Instrument Companies

A two-section continuous type tunnel drier is shown in Fig. 191.
Note that the control system is very similar to that used in the
compartment type drier. When the relative humidity in the wet end
of the tunnel lowers to a predetermined level, the exhaust damper
closes and the dry air circulates without the admission of outside
air or air from the dry end of the tunnel.

Likewise, in the dry end of the tunnel the relative humidity of
the air in the tunnel determines when more of the outside air is to
be admitted.

A saving of heat is effected by using air from the drying end
to aid in drying the incoming product. The product moves from left
to right through the tunnels. Note the direction of motion of the
air is opposite to that of the product in the tunnel. Units of this
type are also used widely in vegetable dehydration.

Building Air Conditioning Application

Fig. 192 illustrates a typical building air conditioning application. The bulbs of the wet and dry bulb transmitter are located

Information Sheet 14

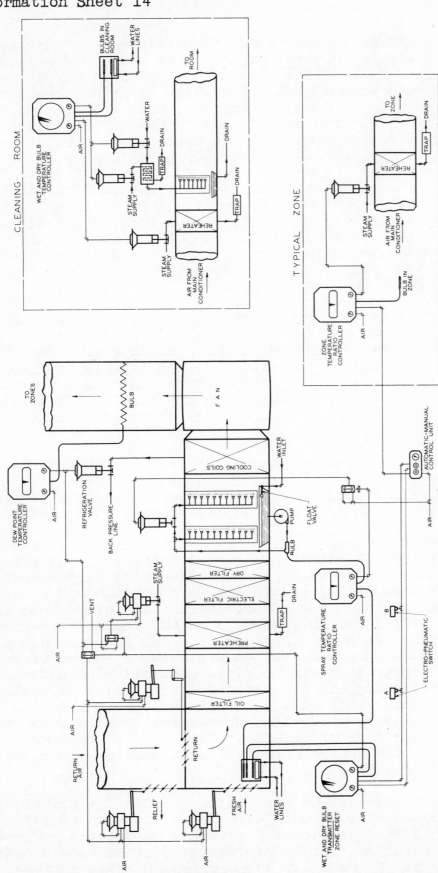

Fig. 192 - Building Air Conditioning Application

Courtesy of Taylor Instrument Companies

Information Sheet 14

in the fresh air stream. The outside temperature, as indicated by
its dry bulb, resets the control point of the zone temperature
controller. Only a typical zone is shown, but there may be many
separate zones, each with a controller which is set by the wet and
dry bulb transmitter. In normal operation, when the outside temperature is below 78°F., the inside temperature is maintained at
74°F. As the outside temperature rises above 78°F., the temperatures in the individual zones are set up proportionally.

An automatic-to-manual control unit is inserted in the line
between the transmitter and the zone controller, so that all the
instruments may be adjusted manually, if desired. If higher or
lower temperatures are desired in any one of the zones, this can be
accomplished by a manual adjustment of the individual zone controller.
The zone controller operates a diaphragm valve in the duct supplying air to that individual zone.

When the wet bulb temperature of the incoming air exceeds 65°F.,
the two non-adjustable three-way pilot valves operate so that the
diaphragm valve in the steam line to the preheater is closed, the
fresh air damper is closed, the return damper is open and the relief
damper is closed. The dew point temperature controller then operates
the refrigeration valve in the back pressure line of the refrigeration system. This acts to control the dew point in the duct feeding
the individual zones.

The dew point temperature controller is set at a temperature
which is the dew point of the desired building temperature. Hence
excess moisture will precipitate at this temperature and be removed.
Any desired reheating is then applied and controlled at each zone.

When the wet bulb temperature of the transmitter is between
52°F. and 65°F., the dew point temperature controller operates the
refrigeration valve in the back pressure line, the diaphragm valve
in the preheater steam line, and the dampers to maintain a satisfactory dry bulb temperature in the duct leading to the various zones.
Below 52°F. the refrigeration system is cut out by Electro-Pneumatic
switch A. When the wet bulb temperature of the incoming air goes
below 50°F., Electro-Pneumatic switch B starts the water circulating
pump so that the spray temperature ratio controller becomes operative.
Under normal conditions, the spray temperature ratio controller maintains the water temperature at a constant value, but when its incoming dry bulb temperature falls to a predetermined value, the water
temperature is lowered in proportion. This in turn reduces the
humidity in all of the zones to prevent condensation of moisture on
the walls of the building.

In this particular set-up, provision is made for a special
cleaning room which is to be maintained at a constant temperature
and relative humidity regardless of external conditions. The wet
and dry bulb temperature controller regulates steam to a Reheater
and the temperature of the water to a series of spray nozzles.

Information Sheet 15   CONTROLLER INSTALLATION

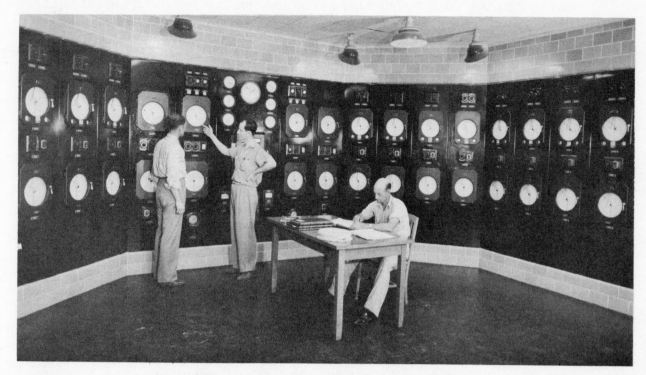

Fig. 193 - A Typical Central Control Panel,
Courtesy of Taylor Instrument Companies

In previous sections of this monograph you have observed a few of the many services which automatic controllers are called upon to perform. You have seen how these devices stand guard over valuable products during their manufacture to protect them from those conditions which would reduce their quality or their usefulness.

The care used in instrument installation pays for itself many times over in providing trouble-free service for a greater period of time, and when trouble does develop, a good installation means that the instrument itself may be tested without shutting down the controlled process. A good installation will also provide a convenient means for switching from automatic to manual control in case of emergency.

The more spectacular installations are those in which a large group of instruments is installed in a central control panel, Fig. 193, where they may be regulating many different operations, such as in a complicated refinery process, or they may be controlling a number of different vats or tanks each of which is performing an operation similar to the other.

While installations of this kind excite the imagination, each of the controllers may be doing no greater service than some isolated, grimy, half-forgotten controller attached directly to a continuous process apparatus.

Information Sheet 15

The advantage of a panel installation lies in the ease with which instrument readings may be compared. Hence, unusual operating conditions are quickly and easily detected and the conditions remedied before they have caused damage to the product. Without a centralized control panel, it may be necessary for the instrument man to spend several hours making his rounds reading individual controller charts, and then even more time may elapse before it is possible to remedy the conditions which he has discovered.

Advantages of Centralized Panel Instrument Mounting

Some of the advantages of a centralized instrument panel installation are as follows:

a. Improved product.
b. Less delay in remedying deviations.
c. Saving of labor.
d. Saving in supervision.
e. Ease of comparison and inspection.
f. Better instrument protection.
g. Instruments receive better care.
h. Improved appearance.

The disadvantages of centralized panel mounting are the increased first cost and long distance transmission difficulties. Of these two, the first factor is usually of greater importance.

Importance of Air Supply

A small jet of air issuing from a nozzle may stand guard over the treasured output of the synthetic rubber plant, the products of the oil refinery, the lumber in kilns, the food in a canner's retort, or the textiles in a dye vat. Each of these services may be as valuable as the product which is being manufactured, and each depends upon the continuance of the flow of air from a small nozzle.

This calls to mind some of the inherent difficulties in producing air at a uniform pressure and keeping it free from moisture, oil particles, or other foreign materials.

The small diameter nozzles used in most controllers might easily become clogged by a tiny particle of carbon or lint; hence a filter or filter strainer is essential.

Without this filter, moisture issuing from the controller nozzle might cause rust or corrosion of the bearings or pivots of the measuring and controlling instrument. Drops of water or of oil in the air supply might cause wide deviations from the desired control point, and while it is not difficult to eliminate the source of these troubles, the delay necessary for this might be a source of real expense.

Information Sheet 15

The selection of the air compressor, supply tank and regulator
which is to be used as a unit air supply source for an air-operated
controller is important. The tank should be of sufficient capacity
to avoid continuous compressor operation and consequent overheating.
The pressure regulator should control the tank pressure within close
limits, avoiding pressure deviations greater than from 1 to 3 pounds.

The supply tank and pipe lines should be equipped with drain
cocks which permit the drainage of condensed moisture. A system of
periodic inspection should be maintained. An air supply drying system is recommended where a large number of instruments is used, to
insure continuous, trouble-free operation.

Factors Affecting Controller Operation

It is often more satisfactory to re-design and re-build or to
replace unsatisfactory process equipment than to try to increase its
efficiency by the simple addition of automatic control. A knowledge
of the factors which affect successful controller operation is necessary if the men who install the equipment are to avoid the errors
which contribute to unsatisfactory control.

Capacity Effect

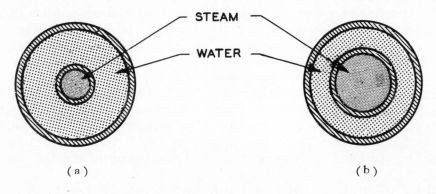

(a)   (b)

Fig. 194

One important factor in securing stable process control is
capacity effect. If we compare, as in Fig. 194, the relative heating effect of a small steam pipe within a large hot water line to
a much larger steam pipe within the same line, we must conclude
that the water would become heated more quickly by the larger pipe
because of the following reasons:

a. Reduced thermal capacity of water to be heated.
b. Increased thermal capacity of the heating media.
c. Increased area for heat conduction.

It should be remembered however, that for most installations of
temperature control equipment, wide fluctuations of temperature are

Information Sheet 15

undesirable, and the system shown in Fig. 194a would be more desirable than that of Fig. 194b, since it would promote more stable control.

Because of the effect of thermal capacity it would be easier to maintain a constant temperature of, say $70^{\circ}F$. in a swimming pool by piping steam through the water than it would be to maintain the same temperature in a pail of water by the same method. Since by admitting even small quantities of steam to the pipes for heating the pail of water, its temperature would go beyond $70^{\circ}F.$, while steam might flow through the pipes in the pool at a rapid rate for a considerable period of time without increasing its temperature more than the mere fraction of a degree.

Apparently, then, there is a definite relationship between the thermal capacity of the heated and the heating elements of a heat exchanger, and its ability to give stabilized control. A high ratio of the thermal capacity of the heated material to that of the material supplying the heat is desirable for stable control. Such a condition is illustrated in Fig. 194a.

Heat Transfer Rate

Another factor affecting temperature controller operation is the rate of heat transfer. The time required for the heat of the steam to pass through the metal of the inside pipe, Fig. 194a, to the water in the outer line, and for its heat to penetrate and thoroughly mix through this water, is the source of what is known as transfer lag. Once the temperature in the outer line has dropped below the control point so that it is necessary to admit more steam to the center pipe, the temperature might continue to drop even after steam has entered the inner pipe provided considerable time was lost in transferring the heat from the pipe to the water. Hence, transfer lag tends to promote unstable control.

A number of conditions affect the rate of heat transfer and thus directly affect transfer lag. Among these are the following:

a. Nature of the product being processed.
b. Condition of the heat transfer surfaces.
c. Air or gas inclusions.
d. Design of the heat exchanger.
e. Difference in temperature between the two transferring media.

Let us examine each of these to determine its effect on transfer lag and on its tendency to promote or prevent stable control.

Any condition which tends to increase the amount of transfer lag will usually increase the tendency toward instability in an automatic controller with the undesirable result of hunting or cycling in the controller.

Information Sheet 15

If the temperature being controlled is that of a non-homogenous product in which large masses of undissolved solid are present in a liquid, these may provide a wide variation in the thermal capacities, and in the rates of conduction of adjacent portions of the product. A homogenous product is more to be desired since then these temperature variations will be avoided.

Transfer of heat from a hot liquid in a pipe line to the surrounding air presents a problem both from the standpoint of capacity effect and of transfer lag.

Transfer of heat from one liquid to another in a heat exchanger may be a very satisfactory process.

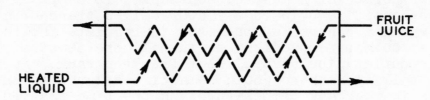

Fig. 195 - Schematic Diagram of a Plate Type
Heat Exchanger

Fig. 195 is a schematic diagram of a plate type heat exchanger in which the cold product, which might be fruit juice, is admitted at the right of the plate type heat exchanger and passes from right to left through the exchanger. The heated liquid which supplies the heat for the pasteurization of the fruit juice enters at the left and passes around and outside the plates containing the fruit juice and proceeds from left to right through the exchanger. It would be possible to arrange a heat exchanger in which the flow of the heat supply would be in the same direction as the flow of the liquid being heated. The heat transfer characteristics of such a system are not as satisfactory, however, as in a system in which the two media flow in opposite directions.

Heat transfer lag is increased if the plate surfaces of a plate-type heat exchanger become coated with mineral deposits, gum or any other substance which is a relatively poor conductor of heat. Any conditions which promote such formations are detrimental to the maintenance of stable and satisfactory control.

Occasionally the readings of a recording controller and a thermometer, both of which are being used to measure the temperature of a single product, do not correspond. In some of these instances it has been found that the temperature sensitive bulb of one or the other of the units has become pocketed in a gas bubble which prevents it from transmitting the true temperature of the product. The presence of any considerable amount of gas in a system designed to

Information Sheet 15

measure liquid temperature will seriously limit the accuracy of the temperature measurement instrument and thus it will also limit the value of the automatic control. Locating the temperature sensitive bulb in a position above the liquid surface where gases may collect, should always be avoided.

Thick, heavy bulbs in air or similar poor conducting media, loose-fitting or poorly conducting wells, or restricted, or insufficient circulation past the sensitive element can produce an appreciable and detrimental transfer lag. This is serious because the thermal element responses should always be rapid in comparison with those of the process being controlled.

Another point which must be considered in properly locating the temperature-sensitive bulb is a factor called transportation lag. In a tank where a controller operates to regulate the tank temperature, it may be more convenient to install the temperature sensitive bulb in the outlet pipe several feet from the tank. Apparently on such an installation there would be a time delay between the time of a change in the tank temperature and the time that such a change could be evaluated by the bulb. An increase in the length of pipe between the tank and the bulb would increase the time required for the material of the tank to be transported through the pipe to the bulb. Hence, this type of time delay in the controller response is often referred to as a transportation lag.

A response delay of this type should be avoided by placing the temperature-sensitive bulb as nearly as possible at the point where the controlled temperature is desired. Transportation lag increases the tendency towards cycling and unstable control.

Certain designs of heat exchangers promote convection currents within the exchanger. These currents add to the difficulty of determining the average temperature or of maintaining a predetermined temperature level throughout the entire volume of the heat exchanger. The type of heat exchanger in which the direction of flow of the liquid supplying the heat is opposite to that of the liquid being heated is more satisfactory for maintaining stable control than are the so-called co-current or cross-current types.

A large difference in temperature between the two heat transferring media is helpful in eliminating heat transfer lag since the amount of heat conducted through a metal plate varies directly with the difference in the temperature of the two plate surfaces.

While high temperature differences are desirable for reducing heat transfer lag, the inertia effects of high temperature difference cannot be overlooked. The time required for the plates of a heat exchanger to cool from a high temperature when the heat supply has been cut off by an automatic controller may emphasize the

Information Sheet 15

tendency of a control system to cycle and often a system with unstable control under high temperature operation will become stable
when operated at a lower temperature.

The following conditions may be said to contribute to stability
of control in an automatic control system:

  a. Low thermal capacity of the heat supplying media.
  b. High thermal conductivity of heat exchanger plates to
     eliminate transfer lag.
  c. Careful design of heat exchanger units.
  d. Proper placement of temperature-sensitive elements to
     avoid transportation lag.
  e. A minimum of temperature difference between supply and
     product.

Transmission Difficulties

In general, long connecting lines are to be avoided in controller installations. Long lines are costly, hard to maintain,
and complicate the solution when trouble arises.

Long lengths of connecting tubing in a temperature measuring
system increase first costs appreciably. Replacement units are difficult to install and repair costs are high. Long lengths of connecting tubing do not impair performance, as is often believed,
because a tube system is a hermetically sealed unit and volume
changes are small. Hence, pressure changes due to these volume
changes can be transmitted readily from bulb to spring end.

In pressure measuring and controlling systems, long lengths of
large piping make control difficult because they contribute to the
transfer lag of the system.

The same is true in considering the connecting piping between
an orifice and a differential pressure measuring instrument or manometer. Also, a manometer when used on a liquid level application
should have the connecting lines as short as possible. In both flow
and liquid level applications, the connecting piping must be free
from sharp bends, be sloped adequately, and air pockets avoided on
liquid flow installations.

Diaphragm control valves should not be located too remotely
from their controllers. Long lengths of air tubing or piping provide many more chances for leaks and contribute adversely to the
over-all time lag of the system, because of the additional volume
which must be supplied or dissipated by the controller when a
change in valve position is called for by the controller.

In many cases the above mentioned 'dont's' can be avoided or

Information Sheet 15

eliminated by remote pneumatic transmission. In this instance, the transmitting instrument is located close to the point of measurement. The transmitter converts the measured variable to a linear air pressure output which is then transmitted by small tubing to a receiving controller which is a pressure-responsive instrument calibrated to the transmitter output. The receiver can be located where convenient to operators and due to the relatively fast response of the pneumatic transmission system, performance is not sacrificed by transmitter tubing lengths as long as 500 feet.

Diaphragm Valve Location

The control valve should always be located where it is accessible for inspection and maintenance, and as previously mentioned, should not be located too remotely from the controller. The control valve is as important to a successful automatic control application as the controller itself, for it must carry out the dictates of the controller.

Shut-off and by-pass valves should be installed around the diaphragm control valve to permit its ready removal for repair or maintenance.

The diaphragm motors and their springs are designed for given operating conditions and for a given direction of flow of the controlling medium through the valve. An arrow on the valve body tells the direction of flow. If the valve is not used under the conditions for which it was designed and built, the control obtainable may be very seriously affected.

Diaphragm valves, in general, operate better and over a longer period of time if installed vertically in horizontal lines. This is because the valve stem moves vertically, whereas if it were installed horizontally, there would be more friction exerted and more wear.

Information Sheet 16   CONTROLLER ADJUSTMENTS

When a new controller and diaphragm valve are installed, the question arises as to just how to adjust the controller in order to produce the best results on the application. Some controllers of the fixed high sensitivity type have so few adjustments that there is little possibility of encountering difficulty. These controllers can be adjusted to open and shut a valve at definite points or through a given band, and if this does not produce the desired result, very little can be done about it. Of course, the adjustments provided by the controller do help to adapt it to the particular process. Adjustability in a controller, however, is of no value if the adjustments are not properly made when the instrument is installed on the application.

While by far the greater number of controllers in the field do not have proportional, automatic reset and rate responses, the adjustment of a controller with these three responses presents the most difficult problem. Therefore, let us consider the methods for adjusting such a controller, realizing that steps may be omitted if the controller lacks a particular response.

For the purpose of this discussion, let us assume that the instrument is in perfect operating condition and that the control valve and auxiliary equipment respond satisfactorily to the output pressure from the controller. Let us also assume that the apparatus to be controlled can be operated satisfactorily and will respond to the changes in the diaphragm valve position. In actual practice, it is a good policy to check both the apparatus and the controller carefully before attempting to place the instrument in control. The instrument may have been damaged in shipping, or it may have been abused when it was installed on the application. Water and dirt are more apt to exist in the air line on a new installation than on an installation which has been in service. The installation may not be properly made; air line connections may not be tight; valves may be in backward; instruments may be connected to the wrong valves, etc. The apparatus to be controlled may not be functioning properly so that satisfactory control will be impossible. Experience proves that all parts of the apparatus should be checked in detail before attempting to place an instrument on control and adjusting it.

Although there are several methods of adjusting the sensitivity, the automatic reset rate, and the rate time, they all lead to the same result. An experienced man will acquire a touch which will enable him to take many short cuts. However, the following method is suggested for a novice.

Start the apparatus on manual control, and maintain the controlled variable within reasonable limits for an appreciable period. Reduce the rate time to zero by opening the needle valve which cuts the rate response unit out of the circuit. With the automatic reset needle valve wide open, or the reset rate set at a rapid value, manipulate the set pointer at any sensitivity until the output pressure from the controller stays between eight and twelve pounds per square inch for a period of several minutes. Close the automatic reset needle valve so that the reset rate is zero, or if this is not possible, set the reset rate to a minimum value. Set the sensitivity of the controller at about twenty pounds per square inch per inch, or the equivalent, and adjust the set pointer on the instrument until the output pressure of the controller is about ten pounds per square inch. The pointer should be reasonably close to the pen, but they may not coincide. Gradually shut the manual control valve and open the hand valve which permits the controlling fluid to flow through the diaphragm valve. If it is important that the process be upset as little as possible, watch the variations which occur, and gradually move the set pointer to open or close the diaphragm valve as desired. If this is carefully done, excessive temperature, pressure, flow, or liquid level variations will be prevented.

If the process cycles, lower the instrument sensitivity. Eventually, a point will be reached where cycling stops. If the process does not cycle or hunt, raise the controller sensitivity until a tendency to hunt occurs, and then lower the sensitivity slightly. When these sensitivity adjustments are made, it may be necessary to manipulate the pointer to avoid excessive disturbances. However, some disturbance is desirable, since the only way to test stability is to produce an upset. The sensitivity should be left at the highest value consistent with good stable performance.

After the sensitivity has been adjusted, gradually open the automatic reset needle valve. Unless the pen and pointer are coincident, a gradual change in the output pressure of the controller will occur, and the pen will tend to approach the set pointer. If the set pointer is not at the desired value, gradually move it to that value so that a major disturbance does not occur. Continue to open the automatic reset needle valve until, when an artificial disturbance is made, there is a definite tendency to cycle. Reduce the automatic reset rate slightly so that a desired degree of stability is attained. The automatic reset rate should be set at the highest value consistent with good stability.

Gradually close the rate response needle valve. After each adjustment, make a small artificial disturbance in the process to make sure that the stability is satisfactory. Eventually, a point will be reached where a further increase in the rate time will reduce the stability materially. Often this point is very sharp, and the process will go into a very violent cycle. The rate time should be set at the highest value consistent with stability.

In many instances, it is now possible to go back to the sensitivity adjustment and increase the sensitivity somewhat due to the presence of the rate response unit. The rate response

Information Sheet 16

effect is a stabilizing influence and permits a higher instrument sensitivity than if it were not available.

This procedure may be shortened considerably if the process is simple or if it is not necessary to avoid disturbances. For example, in adjusting controllers on canners retorts, it is customary to start up empty retorts and adjust the controller without danger of damaging the product. Obviously, under these conditions, a much greater freedom is permitted, and very little manipulation of the set pointer will be required. On continuous processes, water is sometimes used instead of the regular produce so that adjustments can be made without fear of loss. Unfortunately, it is not always possible to have this freedom in adjusting a controller, and it is for these jobs that the previous procedure is recommended.

In this particular connection, it is interesting to note that many controllers are equipped with automatic-to-manual units which facilitate starting up a controller under actual operating conditions. These units vary somewhat in their connections and construction, but their main purpose is to permit cutting in an automatic controller with a minimum disturbance to the product.

In 1941 two methods were advanced by Ziegler and Nichols for adjusting a controller on an application. One of the methods utilized two new factors which were to be determined on the application, namely, the ultimate sensitivity and the ultimate period. In this method, all other control effects except the proportional response are cut out. The sensitivity of the controller is then raised until it is sufficiently high to produce a sustained oscillation. After each adjustment, it is suggested that a disturbance be made, for a process in equilibrium will not start to cycle unless a disturbance does occur. The lowest sensitivity corresponding to a sustained oscillation is called the ultimate sensitivity, S_u, and the period of oscillation is called the ultimate period, P_u. While the stability desired has some bearing on the following equations, the values shown are reasonably accurate for the correct settings of sensitivity S, reset rate R, and rate time T.

Proportional Response

$$S = 0.5S_u$$

Proportional plus Automatic Reset Response
$$S = 0.45S_u, \qquad R = \frac{1.2}{P_u}$$

Proportional plus Automatic Reset plus Rate Response
$$S = 0.6S_u, \qquad R = \frac{2.0}{P_u}, \qquad T = \frac{P_u}{8}$$

Information Sheet 16

To compute the settings of a controller which has proportional plus automatic reset plus rate responses and an ultimate sensitivity of 20 oscillations per minute, first determine the ultimate period. This is equal to 60 seconds divided by 20 or a period of 3 seconds for 1 oscillation. The following computations may then be made:

$$S_u = 20, \qquad P_u = 3$$

Sensitivity

$$S = 0.6S_u, \qquad S = 0.6(20), \qquad S = 12$$

Reset Rate

$$R = \frac{2.0}{P_u}, \qquad R = \frac{2.0}{3}, \qquad R = .66$$

Rate Time (Pre-Act Time)

$$T = \frac{P_u}{8}, \qquad T = \frac{3}{8}, \qquad T = .38$$

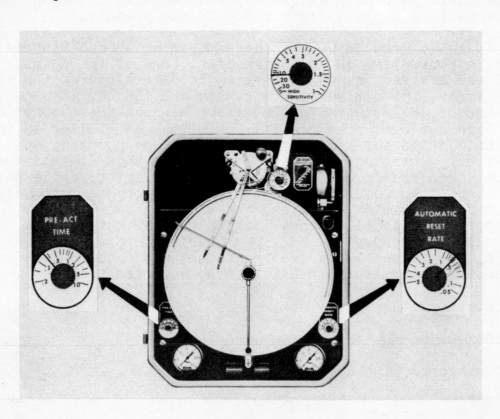

Fig. 196

Fig. 196 shows these settings as they would appear on a controller.

Information Sheet 16

        In general, this method of obtaining the correct adjustment
settings is of value on those applications having a long time lag
on which the more straight forward procedure would require a number
of hours. Whether this method is used or not, these figures will
be found helpful in checking the final instrument setting.

        Another method proposed by Ziegler and Nichols which may be
used on most applications with either short or long time lags
takes into consideration two other process constants, lag and reaction rates.

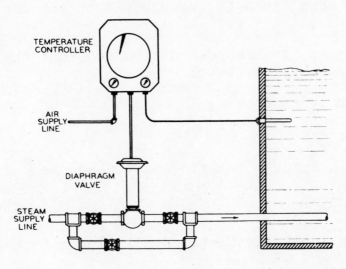

Fig. 197

        To explain this method let us consider a hot water tank, Fig.
197, in which the water temperature is being regulated by the admission of steam by a temperature controller and diaphragm valve.

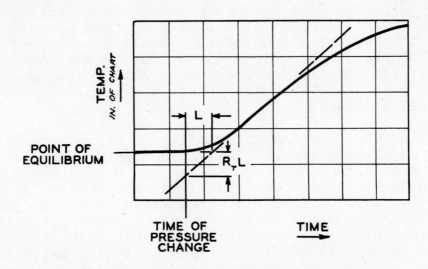

Fig. 198

Information Sheet 16

After a period of equilibrium in which the temperature is neither increasing nor decreasing, a decrease in pressure of 1 psi to the diaphragm valve will produce a chart record similar to the curve shown in Fig. 198. Then the curve is plotted on straight line coordinate paper and a tangent drawn to the curve at the point of the maximum rate of temperature increase. The interval between the time of pressure change and the intersection of the tangent with the horizontal axis at the point of equilibrium is the lag, L. The vertical distance between the horizontal axis at the point of equilibrium and the tangent at the time of the pressure change is equal to R_rL, the product of the reaction rate, R_r, and the lag, L.

By experiment, it has been determined that the following values are reasonably accurate:

Proportional Response

$$S = \frac{1}{R_rL}$$

Proportional plus Automatic Reset Response

$$S = \frac{0.9}{R_rL} , \qquad R = \frac{0.3}{L}$$

Proportional plus Automatic Reset plus Rate Response

$$S = \frac{1.2}{R_rL} , \qquad R = \frac{0.5}{L} , \qquad T = 0.5L$$

While it is not recommended that these formulas be used on every control application, it is an interesting experiment to verify these equations. These formulas, modified slightly, are particularly valuable on applications which are to be equipped with automatic controllers. For example, a hand valve can be moved an amount corresponding to a one-pound change in an automatic control valve. This might be about 1/20 of its maximum travel. The resulting change in the controlled variable could be observed on an indicating or recording device and plotted in the manner illustrated in Fig. 197. If this is done, the controller settings can be predicted with reasonable accuracy before a controller is even purchased for the application.

Unfortunately, the characteristics of a process which determine controller adjustment are not always constant. When loads are light, there is a tendency for the lag and ultimate period of the application to be longer than when loads are heavy. From direct experience, as well as from the formulas set forth by Ziegler and Nichols, this often means that the controller sensitivity, reset rate, and rate time must be adjusted so that stability is obtained under these light load conditions. In a similar way, the reaction

Information Sheet 16

rate and ultimate sensitivity may vary with the load condition. An additional factor which causes the reaction rate to vary from light to heavy loads is the valve characteristic. In some cases, the reaction time will remain more nearly constant with a logarithmic valve characteristic, and in others it will remain more nearly constant with a linear valve characteristic. In any event, some readjustment of the controller settings can be expected after load changes occur. It is usually customary to leave the setting at values which will produce stability under all operating conditions.

Process characteristics do not always remain constant over a prolonged period. For example, heat exchangers may become coated with some insulating material, such as scale and suspended solids. When processes of this type are encountered the controller should be adjusted to meet the new conditions.

GENERAL CHECKING AND TESTING PROCEDURES

When a plant is equipped with automatic controls and other essential instruments, it is done to insure a consistently uniform quality product at minimum cost. Instrument manufacturers try to impress upon users the necessity of proper maintenance of that equipment to assure top efficiency and long service from their investment. It is therefore time and money well spent to keep these units in the highest state of operating efficiency. The following suggestions will materially aid toward this end.

To attain the expected benefits, automatic control must incorporate such characteristics as to render the process practically infallible. The controller, which is entirely mechanical, must draw from constantly dependable sources all factors to give satisfactory performance, such as adequate supply of steam, water, compressed air, or any other product entering into the process. Hence the failure of the controller or anyone of the other factors can result in the disruption of the process. Therefore, when a controller has given satisfaction, it is sound practice, before concluding that the controller is faulty, to always look for a possible explanation in some condition that may have developed external to the instrument itself. Evidence produced by a leaking by-pass valve, improper air supply, obstruction in a supply line, inadequate steam or water supply or faulty steam traps are some of the more common factors which may falsely indicate controller trouble.

Maintenance of Air-Operated Controllers

1. The major working unit in air-operated controllers is the relay air valve. This unit should be cleaned periodically with gasoline or carbon tetrachloride, or in accordance with instructions from the instrument manufacturer.

2. If the instrument is of the recording or indicating type, it should be checked for accuracy, as described later.

3. After the accuracy of the indicating pointer or recording pen has been established, it may be necessary to resynchronize these with the set pointer in some types of automatic controllers. An adjustment is provided for this purpose which should be done in accordance with the manufacturer's instructions.

4. Most controller cases are airtight, hence the cover of the controller should be kept tightly closed at all times to keep out dirt and moisture.

5. Uninterrupted service cannot be obtained unless air supply is reasonably free from oil and dirt. Shut off the air supply when the controller is not in use.

6. Never oil bearings or pivots of levers in controllers.

Information Sheet 17

7. When an instrument is to be taken out of service for any length of time it is well to blow out all connections and to drain any condensate from the air lines to the controller and thoroughly wipe out accumulated moisture and oil from the instrument case.

External Causes for Poor Performance

1. Make certain air supply pressure is sufficient and steady within one pound of that recommended by the manufacturer.

2. On a heating application, involving temperature control, check to determine whether steam supply is sufficient.

3. Check to see if any by-pass valves have been opened in error, or if there is a leak in one of them.

4. Make certain that the diaphragm valve stem moves freely in response to changes of controller air output.

5. Check for leaks in air lines connecting the controller air output to the diaphragm valve. Tighten all unions and piping connections.

Sources of Trouble Within Controller

1. Dirt in the relay air valve. Remove valve and clean internal parts with grease solvent.

2. The restriction or orifice in the nozzle line may be clogged with dirt. This should be cleaned in accordance with manufacturer's instructions.

3. Examine the instrument for leaks around the diaphragm which operates the relay air valve in the controller.

4. Note whether any connecting links have become unfastened or bent out of shape. This is a rare trouble, but it occasionally happens.

5. Examine the nozzle and baffle assembly and make sure that both are free from accumulated grease. Check to see that the nozzle is not plugged.

6. Remove the temperature bulb or other actuating element; subject the sensitive element to a higher value than the control point. If the air gage reading to the diaphragm motor does not change, this is an indication that the actuating element has lost action, and it should be returned to the manufacturer for repairs.

Information Sheet 17

Maintenance of Diaphragm Motor Valves

This unit is often neglected because of its usual trouble-free performance, and frequently inaccessible location. The valve stem must move freely in response to air pressure changes on the diaphragm. If jerky action is noted:

1. Determine whether the rubber diaphragm is in good condition. If it is no longer pliable, it should be replaced.

2. Check whether the packing in stuffing box is compressed too tightly. Only finger-tip tightness of packing nut is desirable. If repacking is necessary, follow the instructions furnished by the manufacturer.

3. Examine the valve disc and seat for leakage and determine whether any foreign material has become lodged between them, thereby restricting the valve stem travel.

4. The valve spring may have deteriorated excessively due to rusting. Although spring life is generally very long, it should then be replaced with a new spring.

Recording Mechanism Maintenance and Checking

To obtain the maximum uninterrupted service from any recording type instrument, a few simple precautions should be followed.

1. Do not mount the instrument where it is subjected to vibration.

2. Do not unnecessarily kink or bend the flexible tubing or piping on temperature and pressure instruments.

3. Occasionally wash out dried ink from the pen with hot water or alcohol to assure clear records at all times.

4. Do not wind clock too tightly. Clock movement should be cleaned and re-oiled by competent clock repair men approximately yearly. If an electric clock is used, no maintenance is required.

5. Be sure the pen does not bear too hard on the chart. Pen pressure should be only sufficient for ink to flow on to the chart.

6. When placing a chart on an instrument, be sure that it is accurately centered on the chart driving arbor.

7. When washing down equipment, do not play water directly on the case.

8. Do not attempt changing the accuracy of pen indication unless very definite evidence of inaccuracy exists.

Checking the Recording Pen

The following checking procedure is built up as applying to a recording thermometer, or temperature controller. However, the same procedure is applied for other means of actuation. If it is certain that the recorder pen does not indicate correct temperature, the following procedure should be followed in testing an instrument used at temperatures below 212°F., such as will be very frequently encountered.

The bulb should be removed from the apparatus and placed in a water bath whose temperature is approximately that at which the instrument is normally used. Fully immerse the bulb along with a test thermometer of known accuracy. Vigorously agitate the water with a paddle or similar stirring device, and after a period of at least two minutes, or until the recorder pen comes to rest, compare the pen indication with that of the thermometer. Quickly reset the pen position by means of the micrometer screw to agree with the temperature indicated by the standard thermometer.

For temperatures above 212°F. the bulb can be placed in a steam log or checked in an oil bath by a similar procedure.

The above procedure is sufficient for most cases of inaccuracy. However, infrequently a recorder when adjusted to read correctly at a low point on the chart will not read correctly at a point near the upper limit of the chart. When a condition of this kind occurs, the instrument is said to be out of calibration, and it is recommended that the user refer to the instructions supplied by the manufacturer.

After prolonged usage, or as a result of mechanical injury, the actuating system may become inoperative. This is indicated by the fact that the pen arm does not move when the bulb temperature is changed, and may be caused by leakage of the actuating medium. Not in all cases will a leak result in the recorder becoming sufficiently inaccurate to be readily apparent. Sometimes the actuating coil continues to move but in progressively smaller amounts for a given bulb temperature change. This has led to making adjustments which only restore accurate readings at a given temperature for brief periods. If the thermal element becomes inoperative or unstable, it should be returned to the manufacturer for repairs.

If the chart revolves too fast or too slow, correction can be made by adjusting the regulator of the clock, if it is of the spring driven type.

If the clock is of the electric type, no adjustment is possible.

Information Sheet 17

Usually an electric clock functions accurately or is completely inoperative due to failure of the field coil or internal gearing, in which case factory replacement is required.

Incorrect adjustment of the pen will prevent the pen from following the time arc on the chart, thereby making it appear that the chart is not revolving at correct speed. This condition is especially noticeable when the pen is caused to move over a large portion of the chart in a short interval.

To check the pen adjustment, move the pen across the chart by alternately immersing the bulb in hot and cold water, or disconnecting the link from the Bourdon tube and moving it by hand. Bend the point of the pen upward if it gains in time indication with reference to time arc on the chart, when moving from a high to low temperature. Bend the point downward if the reverse is true. Before making any adjustment of the pen, make sure that it is properly located on the pen arm.

If the pen moves jerkily, this is an indication either of excessive friction in the mechanism, or excessive pressure between the pen and the chart. Excessive mechanism friction is usually caused by corrosion of the pivots in the movement or bent links, if any are present. This condition can be remedied readily by cleaning the parts in a solvent such as carbon tetrachloride, and rebending the levers or links until friction is eliminated, as indicated by the pen returning to the same position on the chart when the pen arm is moved manually a slight amount both above and below a fixed point. Excessive pen pressure should be relieved by grasping the pen arm near the upper end and bending the pen arm slightly away from the chart.

Appendix I   GLOSSARY OF TERMS

ACCURACY (1)

A numerical value which defines the limit of error of a measurement, usually in per cent of an instrument scale.

(1)
AUTOMATIC CONTROL (or Regulation)

The act of maintaining the indicated value of a variable within prescribed limits, or of varying the value of the variable according to a desired time quantity relation.

AUTOMATIC CONTROLLER
(or Regulator) (2)

A mechanism which measures the value of a quantity or condition subject to change with time, and operates to maintain within limits this measured value.

AUTOMATIC RESET RESPONSE (3)

An output pressure change, which proceeds at a rate dependent upon the proportional response resulting from a control point deviation. It acts in the same direction as proportional response and continues until the set point and control point are coincident.

CAPACITY LAG (1)

A process lag (q.v.) which results in a retardation of the detection of a change in value of a variable due to energy or material capacity.

CONTROL AGENT (2)

That process energy or material whose flow is directly varied by a final control element.

CONTROL BAND

See throttling range.

CONTROL ELEMENT

See final control element.

CONTROL POINT (2)

That value of a controlled variable which an automatic controller operates to maintain.

CONTROLLED VARIABLE (2)

A quantity or condition which is measured and controlled by an automatic controller.

CONTROLLER (instrument) LAG (1)

Delay in effecting correction of a change in a controlled variable due to a delay or retardation in any part of a control instrument.

CONTROLLING MEANS (2)

Of an automatic controller, consists of those elements which, acting together, produce corrective action based upon the information supplied by the measuring means.

(1) Reprinted by permission of Chemical and Metallurgical Engineering.
(2)   "   "   "   "   A.S.M.E. (These terms have not yet been officially adopted, hence they are subject to change.)
(3) Reprinted by permission of Taylor Instrument Companies.

Appendix I

CORRECTIVE ACTION (2)

A change in the flow of the control agent initiated by the measuring means of an automatic controller.

(2)
CORRESPONDING CONTROLLER ACTION

That in which there is a predetermined relation between values of the controlled variable and positions of final control element.

DAMPING (1)

Effect due to whatever cause, tending to hinder or prevent oscillation.

DEAD TIME (2)

Any definite delay period between the time when a change occurs in a control agent and the time when that change affects the controlled variable at the point of measurement.

DEAD TIME (1)

See process lag.

DEAD ZONE (1)

Range of measured values of a variable in which an instrument cannot detect or initiate corrections of a change.

DERIVATIVE CONTROLLER ACTION (2)

That in which there is a predetermined relation between a derivative function of the controlled variable and the position of a final control element.

DEVIATION (1)

Departure of the value of a variable from the desired or normal value.

DIRECT ACTING CONTROLLER (3)

One adjusted to give an increasing air output pressure with an increase in the variable whether it is temperature, pressure, vacuum flow or liquid level, and regardless of the direction of pen or pointer travel which indicates the increase.

DISTANCE-VELOCITY LAG (1)

Delay in detection of a change in a measured value of a variable due to the need to transport material to the point of measurement.

DRIFT (2)

A sustained deviation. In a corresponding controller, drift results from the predetermined relation between values of the controlled variable and positions of the final control element.

DRIFT (1)

See Droop.

DROOP (1)

Shift in equilibrium or average value of a variable owing to an inherent characteristic of an automatic controller.

DROOP CORRECTION (Also drift) (1)

See proportional-plus-reset.

Appendix I

FINAL CONTROL ELEMENT (2)

That portion of the controlling means which directly varies a control agent.

FLOATING CONTROL (1)

Type of control action which varies a flow without a definite relation other than direction of change, with the value of the variable.

FLOATING CONTROLLER ACTION (2)

That in which there is a predetermined relation between values of the controlled variable, and rate of motion of a final control element, with or without a neutral zone.

FLOATING RATE (2)

Applying to proportional plus floating controller action, is expressed in units of the number of times per unit time that the effect of proportional position action is reproduced by proportional speed floating action.

FLOATING SPEED (2)

Applying to floating controller action, is the rate of movement of a final control element corresponding to a specified deviation. It is conveniently expressed in per cent of full range of movement per unit of time.

FLOATING TIME (2)

Applying to proportional plus floating controller action, is the reciprocal of floating rate.

FOLLOW-UP (1)

Device which is used with relay elements in controllers to establish a definite control response for a given change in variable by setting up a counter response.

HUNTING (1)

Controller cycling or oscillation.

INDICATION (1)

Measurement of the instantaneous value of a variable.

INDUSTRIAL INSTRUMENT (1)

Device for measuring or measuring and controlling the values of a process variable.

LOAD ERROR

See droop.

MEASUREMENT (1)

Indication of the instantaneous value of a process variable.

MEASURING ELEMENT (1)

Part of an instrument which indicates instantaneous values of a variable.

MEASURING MEANS (2)

Of an automatic controller consists of those elements which are involved in ascertaining and communicating to the controlling means the magnitude of the controlled variable.

Appendix I

MULTIPOSITION CONTROL (1)

Type of control response which selects one of several definite rates of corrective action, depending on the deviation of a process variable.

MULTIPOSITION CONTROLLER ACTION (2)

That in which there are three or more predetermined positions of a final control element corresponding to definite values of the variable.

MULTISPEED FLOATING CONTROLLER ACTION (2)

That in which there are two or more speeds of the final control element, each corresponding to a definite range of values of the controlled variable.

NEUTRAL ZONE (2)

Of an automatic controller, is a predetermined range of values of the controlled variable, within which no control action occurs.

NON-CORRESPONDING (1)

See floating controller action.

OFFSET

See droop.

ON-AND-OFF CONTROL

See two-position control.

PILOT VALVE (1)

Device for controlling the flow of an auxiliary fluid used to amplify the power of a controller measuring system in effecting control.

PLANT (2)

Comprises the apparatus in which a variable is to be controlled.

POSITIONING CONTROL

See proportional control.

POWER UNIT (2)

A mechanism of a relay-operated controller which applies power to move a final control element in response to changes in relay output.

PRE-ACT RESPONSE (3)

An output pressure change, additive to the proportional response, which has a magnitude dependent upon the rate of the proportional response changes.

PRE-ACT TIME (3)

The interval at which the output of an instrument with pre-act precedes that of one with proportional response alone, when the pen moves at a constant rate.

PRECISION (1)

Closeness of agreement of repeated measurements of the same quantity.

PRIMARY SENSITIVE ELEMENT (1)

Device which senses change in a process variable and determines magnitude of change, without indication.

PROCESS (2)

Comprises the collective functions performed in and by a plant or equipment in which a variable is to be controlled.

Appendix I

PROCESS CHARACTERISTICS (2)

Comprise those physical characteristics related to the problem of automatic control. Factors which determine process characteristics include those associated with material being processed and those representing the effect of automatic controllers applied to the process, other than the particular one under consideration, in addition to those associated with the process proper.

PROCESS LAG (1)

Includes capacity lags, transfer lag, distance-velocity lag and reaction lag, any retardation or delay in bringing information concerning a change in variable to the primary sensitive element of an instrument.

PROCESS VARIABLE

See variable; related specifically to processes.

PROPORTIONAL BAND (2)

Applying to proportional position controller action, is the range of scale values through which the controlled variable must pass in order that the final control element be moved through its entire range.

PROPORTIONAL BAND

See throttling range.

PROPORTIONAL CONTROL (1)

Type of control response which adjusts the final control element to a definite relation with the measured value of the variable.

PROPORTIONAL PLUS FLOATING CONTROLLER ACTION (2)

That in which proportional position and proportional speed floating action are additively combined.

PROPORTIONAL-PLUS-RESET CONTROL (1)

Type of proportional control which eliminates droop.

PROPORTIONAL POSITION CONTROLLER ACTION (2)

That in which there is a continuous linear relation between the position of a final control element and the value of the controlled variable.

PROPORTIONAL-POSITION CONTROL

See proportional control.

PROPORTIONAL RESPONSE

See proportional control.

PROPORTIONAL SPEED FLOATING CONTROLLER ACTION (2)

That in which there is a continous linear relation between the rate of motion of a final control element and the deviation of the controlled variable.

PYROMETER (1)

Device for measuring high temperatures.

REACTION LAG (1)

Process lag due to the time necessary to complete a reaction before the result of the reaction can be measured.

Appendix I

RELAY (1)

Usually means electrical relay, but also used to designate other amplifying means such as a relay air valve.

RELAY OPERATED CONTROLLER (or Regulator)(2)

One in which the motion or force developed by the measuring means is used to operate an amplifying relay, the output from which operates the final control element, either directly or through additional relays.

RELAY OUTPUT (2)

That portion of the relay supply which is transmitted to the power unit or to another relay.

RELAY SUPPLY (2)

The auxiliary energy supplied to a relay.

RESET (1)

See proportional-plus-reset. If automatic reset, a type of control response giving a rate of valve movement proportional to deviation of the variable.

RESET RATE (3)

The rate of change of output pressure in psi per minute resulting from a sustained one pound per square inch change in proportional response output pressure from equilibrium at the control point.

SCALE ERROR

Difference between true and indicated values of a variable.

SECOND DERIVATIVE CONTROL (1)

Type of control response giving a rate of final control element movement proportional to the acceleration of the change in deviation.

SELF-ACTING (or operating) CONTROLLER (1)

Type of controller employing the power of the measuring system without amplification by an auxiliary power source, to effect necessary corrective action.

SELF-ACTUATED CONTROLLER (or Regulator) (2)

One in which all the energy necessary to operate the final control element is supplied by the measuring element.

SELF-REGULATION (2)

That operating characteristic which inherently assists or opposes the establishment of equilibrium. In the latter case the self-regulation is said to be negative.

SENSITIVE ELEMENT

See primary sensitive element.

SENSITIVITY (1)

Ratio of effect to cause in an instrument, such as ratio of valve movement to pen movement.

SERVO, SERVO MOTOR (1)

Auxiliary power-operated amplifying device used in instruments to position final control element under control of the measuring element.

Appendix I

SET POINT (3)

Of a controller, is the point on the chart or scale indicated by the set pointer.

SINGLE-SPEED FLOATING CONTROLLER ACTION (2)

That in which there is a single rate of motion of the final control element.

STABLE CONTROL (2)

Control in which the value of the controlled variable is maintained within, or returned within, desirable limits without sustained oscillation.

THREE-POSITION CONTROL

See multi-position control.

THROTTLING CONTROL (1)

Type of control which is able to position its final control element at any position between maximum and minimum limits. Sometimes means proportional, only.

THROTTLING RANGE (ZONE) (1)

Range of measured values needed to cause maximum possible change in final control element setting, usually expressed in per cent of full instrument scale.

TRANSFER LAG (1)

Retardation in effect of change in variable on primary sensitive element due to capacity effects or resistances on supply side.

TWO-POSITION CONTROL (1)

Type of control response in which final control element can be positioned only at a maximum or minimum position.

TWO-POSITION DIFFERENTIAL GAP CONTROLLER ACTION (2)

Two-position action in which a final control element is moved in one direction at a predetermined value of the controlled variable, and subsequently in the other direction only after the value of the variable has crossed a "differential" gap to a second predetermined value.

TWO-POSITION SINGLE-POINT CONTROLLER ACTION (2)

Refers to the particular case of two-position action in which the predetermined values are identical.

VARIABLE (1)

Physical quantity which is variable with time.

Appendix II   ADVANCED CONTROL THEORY

In a previous section, it has been shown that the satisfactory control of a variable in a unit process cannot always be obtained by the simple open and shut manipulation of a control valve. On the contrary, for most accurate control, the valve must be carefully moved at varying rates and varying amounts in response to the physical quantity being controlled. By making certain assumptions, a simple control theory may be developed with the assistance of a little mathematics. This theory is very helpful in explaining the behavior of automatic control systems and provides a background for understanding the limitations of automatic controllers.

Assumptions:

1. The automatic control system measures the variable accurately.

2. The automatic control system repeats. It always does the same thing to the valve when the controlled variable repeats a previous action. For example, if temperature is being controlled and it falls 10°F. in 1 minute so the control valve moves from 1/2 to 3/4 open in that interval, then every time the temperature falls 10°F. in 1 minute, the valve moves from 1/2 to 3/4 open, assuming that the conditions at the beginning of the fall were identical. This might be stated in another way, namely, that the controller must perform consistently. It cannot respond differently at two times to the same stimulae.

3. The controller is an air-operated recording or indicating controller so that the input can be measured by the movement of the pen or pointer on the chart or scale and the output can be measured by the change in the output air pressure.

This assumption introduces a great simplification since it allows the results to be applied to any measured variable and eliminates the vagaries of the control valve from the discussion. The theory will later be broadened to include electrical and hydraulic actuation as well as non-indicating controllers.

If the controller has a response which is proportional to the deviation of the pen from the original value, then

$$(1) \qquad\qquad P - P_O = S(X - X_O)$$

where $(X - X_O)$ is the movement of the pen in inches, and P_O is the original output pressure in pounds per square inch corresponding to X_O, and P is the new output pressure in pounds per square inch corresponding to X. S is the constant of proportionality and its

Appendix II

dimensions may be determined from the equation:

(1a) $$S = \frac{P - P_O}{X - X_O}$$ where S = pounds per square inch per inch

Now if the change $(X - X_O)$ takes place over a period of time $(t - t_O)$, then $\frac{X - X_O}{t - t_O}$ is the average rate of change of X and $\frac{P - P_O}{t - t_O}$ is the average rate of change of P.

The equation may be written:

(1b) $$\frac{P - P_O}{t - t_O} = S\left(\frac{X - X_O}{t - t_O}\right)$$

It is customary to designate extremely small differences of pressure such as might be obtained by subtracting $P - P_O$, by calling such a small quantity a differential and designating it as dP meaning a pressure differential. Likewise, extremely small values of temperature such as $t - t_O$ would be called temperature differentials and could be referred to as dt, while those of $X - X_O$ would be simply dX.

Now, if $(X - X_O)$ is made very small, $(t - t_O)$ and $(P - P_O)$ become very small, and we may let $(P - P_O)$ equal dP, $(t - t_O)$ equal dt and $(X - X_O)$ equal dX. Then the equation may be written:

(1c) $$\frac{dP}{dt} = S\left(\frac{dX}{dt}\right)$$

This is the mathematical way of stating that the rate of change of output pressure is <u>proportional</u> to the rate of movement of the pen or pointer. Now, in many controllers S is adjustable over a wide range and this adjustability is required to adapt the controller to various processes. When S has a low value, say 1 psi per inch, the output pressure changes only 1 psi when the pen or pointer moves through 1 in. on the chart or scale. This means that the opening and closing of the control valve is spread over a relatively broad band, a condition which promotes stability as previously shown. When S has a high value, say 1000 psi per inch, the output pressure changes 1 psi when the pen or pointer moves through 0.001 in. on the chart or scale. The opening and closing of the control valve occurs over a very narrow band approaching an on-off action. For this reason, in air-operated control systems, controllers with a value of S of 1000 or more are often classed with the on-off electrical controllers, even though they are not truly in this group. As the value of S increases, more and more valve action results from a given change in the controlled variable, so eventually an instability or "hunting" occurs. Controllers are usually adjusted so that S has its

Appendix II

highest value consistent with good stability.

If the controller has a response which is proportional to the _rate_ of deviation of the pen from the original value, then

(2) $$(P - P_O) = K_1\left(\frac{dX}{dt}\right)$$

where K_1 is a constant of proportionality. This equation may also be written:

(2a) $$P - P_O = K_1\left(\frac{X - X_O}{t - t_O}\right)$$

where $(X - X_O)$ is the movement of the pen in inches in the time $(t - t_O)$.

Now, while K_1 may be entirely independent of S, most air-operated controllers are designed so that K_1 is directly proportional to S. If T is a new constant of proportionality, then

(2b) $$K_1 = TS$$

Equation (2) and (2a) become:

(2c) $$P - P_O = TS\left(\frac{dX}{dt}\right)$$

(2d) $$P - P_O = TS\left(\frac{X - X_O}{t - t_O}\right)$$

Now the dimensions of the new constant T may be determined from the equation:

(2e) $$T = \frac{(P - P_O)(t - t_O)}{S(X - X_O)} \qquad \text{but } S = \frac{P - P_O}{X - X_O}$$

(2f) Hence $$T = \frac{(\text{pounds per sq. in.})(\text{inches})(\text{minutes})}{(\text{pounds per sq.in.})(\text{inches})} = \text{minutes}$$

Then T is a time constant of the equation and in process controllers, it is usually expressed in minutes. This variable which can be adjusted through a wide range on many controllers is often called 'rate time'. In process control, a rate time T of 0.1 minutes is relatively short, and a rate time of 10 minutes is relatively long.

This control response has several names which are in general use, including pre-act, preset, rate and derivative. The first two are based in the fact that with any given rate of change of the pen or pointer on the controller, the output pressure will have a value which would not otherwise be reached until T minutes later, if this response were not available. Thus, this response provides a

Appendix II

preliminary action. Note, however, that the variable must actually move at a tangible rate before any response is obtained.

As in the case with the sensitivity adjustment S, the rate time T can be set at too great a value causing instability or "hunting". It also may be set at so low a value (zero) that it has no effect at all. Best control is usually obtained with the rate time set at the highest value consistent with good stable performance. It is always adjusted after the sensitivity S has been set at its most satisfactory value.

According to procedures of Calculus, equation (2c) may be differentiated to obtain:

(2g)
$$\frac{dP}{dt} = TS\left(\frac{d^2X}{dt^2}\right)$$

If the controller has a response whose rate is proportional to the deviation of the pen from the original value, then

(3)
$$\frac{dP}{dt} = K_2(X - X_0)$$

where K_2 is the constant of proportionality. This equation may also be written:

(3a)
$$\frac{P - P_0}{t - t_0} = K_2(X - X_0)$$

where $(P - P_0)$ is the change in the output pressure in the time $(t - t_0)$.

While K_2 may be independent of S, most air-operated controllers are designed so that K_2 is directly proportional to S. If R is a new constant of proportionality, then

(3b)
$$K_2 = RS$$

Equation (3) and (3a) become

(3c)
$$\frac{dP}{dt} = RS(X - X_0)$$

(3d)
$$\frac{P - P_0}{t - t_0} = RS(X - X_0)$$

Again, the dimensions of the new constant R may be determined from the equation:

(3e)
$$R = \frac{(P - P_0)}{S(X - X_0)(t - t_0)} \qquad \text{but } S = \frac{P - P_0}{X - X_0}$$

Appendix II

(3f) $R = \dfrac{(\text{pounds per sq. in.})(\text{inches})}{(\text{pounds per sq. in.})(\text{inches})(\text{minutes})} = \dfrac{1}{\text{minutes}}$

Thus R is a rate constant in the equation and in process controllers it is called the reset rate. By comparing equations (3d) and (1), it can be seen that this response is $R(t - t_0)$ times the proportional response. In other words, this response repeats the proportional response R times each minute. For this reason, the calibration R is really "repeats per minute".

In industrial process control, 10 repeats per minute is a large value of R, while 0.1 repeats per minute is a small value of R. As the value of the reset rate R is increased on any process, a point is reached where instability or "hunting" occurs. At the other extreme the reset rate may be set at zero which eliminates this control response. The most satisfactory setting of R is the highest value consistent with stability. The reset rate is usually adjusted to its correct value after the best sensitivity S and rate time T are determined.

By adding the equations (1d), (2g) and (3c) the response of a controller with all three control effects may be obtained.

(4) $\dfrac{dP}{dt}(\text{Total}) = RS(X - X_0) + S\left(\dfrac{dX}{dt}\right) + TS\left(\dfrac{d^2X}{dt^2}\right)$

Now, from direct reasoning it is hard to show the need for other control effects or responses, but the above equation suggests the possibility of these control effects. A complete controller, for example, might consist of an infinite number of control effects with corresponding adjustments, as indicated by the following equations:

(5) $\dfrac{dP}{dt}(\text{Complete}) = \ldots QS(X - X_0)^2 + RS(X - X_0) + S\left(\dfrac{dX}{dt}\right)$ ST

$\dfrac{d^2X}{dt^2} + SU\left(\dfrac{d^3X}{dt^3}\right) \ldots \ldots$

While it cannot be denied that a controller with these additional control effects offers the possibility of better control of a process variable, it must be admitted that the improvement which could be obtained over the controller with three control effects rarely would justify the added cost and complication. In fact, at present, only a few of the industrial control applications require more than one or two of the control effects of equation (4).

Now while equation (4) applies particularly well to pneumatic control systems which record or indicate, it may be adapted to non-indicating controllers and to electrical and hydraulic controllers by substitution. Let $(V - V_0)$ be the movement of the

Appendix II

control valve and $(y - y_o)$ be the corresponding change in the controlled variable. Equation (4) becomes

(6) $$\frac{dv}{dt}(\text{Total}) = A(y - y_o) + B\left(\frac{dy}{dt}\right) + C\left(\frac{d^2y}{dt^2}\right)$$

where the new constants A, B and C have the dimensions:

A = rate of valve movement per minute per unit change in the controlled variable ($1^oF.$, $1^oC.$, 1 psi, etc.)

B = valve movement per unit change in the controlled variable

C = valve movement per unit rate of change of the controlled variable.

This equation (6) must be used when the response of two dissimilar control systems must be compared, assuming that they operate on the same valve under otherwise identical conditions. When this is not so, the equation (6) may be made even more general, assuming that F is the flow of the controlling fluid and y is the variation in the controlled medium.

(7) $$\frac{dF}{dt}(\text{Total}) = A_1(y - y_o) + B_1\left(\frac{dy}{dt}\right) + C_1\left(\frac{d^2y}{dt^2}\right)$$

where A_1, B_1 and C_1 are new constants.

INDEX

INDEX (continued)

INDEX (continued)

INDEX (continued)